The Wright Brothers

Pioneers of Power Flight

IMMORTALS OF SCIENCE

The Wright Brothers
Pioneers of Power Flight

by Carroll V. Glines

FRANKLIN WATTS, INC.
575 Lexington Avenue
New York, N.Y. 10022

Jacket photo courtesy
U.S. Air Force

FOURTH PRINTING

SBN 531-00934-3

Copyright © 1968 by Franklin Watts, Inc.
Library of Congress Catalog Card Number: 68-10635
Printed in the United States of America

Dedication
To
Major General Benjamin D. Foulois
Last of the First to Fly

Contents

CHAPTER I

The Flight of the Flyer

THE fishermen's shanties along the waterfront at Kitty Hawk, North Carolina, stood bleak and lifeless on the morning of December 17, 1903. There was a coating of ice on the puddles left from the rain of the day before. Sea gulls, screeching in their constant quest for food, soared back and forth along the beach. The wind, bitter and cold, blasted the sand from the dunes. As the breakers rolled toward the beach, their tops were ripped off and turned into mist. It did not seem like a day when history would be made.

Kill Devil Hill, four miles south of Kitty Hawk, was barren and dreary even though the sun rose early into a near-cloudless sky. By ten thirty the wind had died down a little, and two men hauled a flimsy, kitelike contraption out of a wooden shack. Within the next hour and a half on that sandy hill in a remote section of the East Coast, two unknown bicycle repairmen would fly in a powered "aeroplane" four times. The

1

first flight would go 120 feet and last only twelve seconds; the fourth, 852 feet and last fifty-nine seconds.

The two men, Orville and Wilbur Wright, later wrote of that first twelve-second flight as "the first in the history of the world in which a machine carrying a man had raised itself by its own power into the air in free flight, had sailed forward on a level course without reduction of speed, and had finally landed without being wrecked."

After the last flight took place at noon, the airplane, which the Wrights called a "Flyer," was placed behind a sand dune to protect it from the wind. However, a few moments later a gust lifted the machine up on one wing and damaged it enough to call a halt to the experiments. The two men packed up their gear and trudged the four miles to the weather bureau's station at Kitty Hawk. They asked the weather observer if he would use his government telegraph to send a message to Norfolk, where it would be relayed to one of the commercial telegraph offices and forwarded to Dayton, Ohio.

Orville, the younger brother, wrote out the message addressed to their father, the Reverend Milton Wright:

SUCCESS FOUR FLIGHTS THURSDAY MORNING ALL AGAINST TWENTY-ONE-MILE WIND STARTED FROM LEVEL WITH ENGINE POWER ALONE AVERAGE SPEED THROUGH AIR THIRTY-ONE MILES LONGEST FIFTY-NINE SECONDS INFORM PRESS HOME CHRISTMAS.

ORVILLE WRIGHT.

Although the Wright brothers knew that they had

finally been able to attach an engine to a glider and get that combination into the air, there is no indication that they were aware of the enormity of their achievement or of its possible impact on the future of the world. Actually, they had done something that man had been striving toward since recorded history began.

That first airplane which carried a man under its own power was, by today's standards, a very fragile creation. Its two wings were made of wood and covered with muslin fabric. They were joined by wooden struts reinforced with wire. Held out in front of the main wings were two smaller wings that acted much as modern airplane elevators and horizontal stabilizers do to control the flight of the ship. Parallel rudders were held by wooden supports behind the wings. There was no fuselage, or enclosed body; the pilot lay prone on the bottom wing next to the engine. Two pusher propellers were geared to the engine by bicycle sprockets and chains. Where today's aircraft have wheels or pontoons, the Wright Flyer had skids. It looked something like a box kite. In fact, that is just about what it was, since the brothers had actually evolved their airplane from a box kite.

As children in Ohio, the Wright brothers had been expert and devoted kite builders and flyers. As adults, their interest in kiting led them to read and reread the literature of aeronautics, the science of flight. For years, while their bicycle manufacturing and repairing business prospered, they discussed gliding experiments and the principles of gliding.

After successful experiments in controlling gliders, the brothers constructed their first man-carrying glider in 1900. They chose Kitty Hawk, North Carolina, as the site of their experiments because the government, after some research, informed them that they could be assured of plenty of room and a constant wind there. In all their flights that year, they managed to spend a total of only two minutes in the air.

The next year they were back at Kitty Hawk with another kitelike glider, this time heavier and built along known aerodynamic principles, plus a few of the Wrights' own innovations. The great Octave Chanute, a pioneer student of aeronautics, watched their experiments with the device tethered, and later in free flight. The results, both in control and in weight carried, were the best ever achieved by anyone up to that time.

Yet the Wrights still had many aerodynamic problems to overcome before their machine could really be said to work well. In August, 1902, they returned to Kitty Hawk with a new glider. This time they were jubilant. In all, between August and October, they accomplished some one thousand gliding flights and learned how to control their flimsy craft in winds up to thirty-six miles per hour. At that stage in the development of the airplane these were incredible performances. The Wright brothers returned to Dayton convinced that they were ready to fly a powered craft successfully.

The significance of these early Wright experiments cannot be overestimated. Many attempts had been made previously to build successful gliders and powered aircraft. None of the gliders ever proved efficient, because the only means of giving a glider stability was by shifting the pilot's weight. No early experimenter ever knew, when he first tried to fly a man-carrying powered airplane, how he could control it. On the other hand, the Wrights developed a means of control with a kite even before trying to fly a glider. And before they had any success in gliding they worked out basic scientific data on lift and drag. And before they tried powered flight they had mastered the problems of stability, control, and balance in a glider.

Although not college-educated scientists, these two men had applied scientific methods of thinking to their problem. They had dared to think differently and independently. Their persistence, ingenuity, and initiative allowed them to achieve what other men could not. So it was on that cold morning of December 17, 1903, that Orville and Wilbur Wright solved the riddle of flying and forever altered the course of history.

CHAPTER II

At Home in Ohio

THE Wright brothers were not scientists in the usual sense. They had not gone to college, studied mathematics and scientific subjects, and then applied this knowledge to solve heavier-than-air aerodynamic problems. They were, however, "trial-and-error" scientists, who read everything they could find on the subject of flight and duplicated the experiments of other men. To their disappointment, none of the theories expressed by others who had tried to fly ever worked. The Wrights concluded that no one really knew why gliders glided and why kites stayed up in the air. Yet they persisted and eventually found the secret.

What were these men like? What was their background? What events had led them to that magic moment when one of them defied gravity and scored one of the most important technological "firsts" of all time?

If the Wrights can be called geniuses, perhaps heredity played an important part in giving them mechanical ability, the ability to think creatively, and the will-power to continue experimenting in spite of continual failure. Their mother's father—John G. Koerner—migrated to the United States from Germany in 1818 to escape the tyranny of a militaristic government. He was a superb maker of farm wagons and carriages, with a reputation for doing his own thinking and not believing anything without conclusive proof. Grandfather Koerner settled in Union County, Indiana, where the Koerner carriages became famous for their dependability and sturdy construction.

On their paternal side, the Wrights descended from similar sturdy pioneers, who had migrated to Cincinnati, Ohio, in 1790. Their grandfather Dan Wright married and settled in Rush County, Indiana, where Milton, father of Wilbur and Orville, was born in a log cabin in 1828.

Dan Wright was a farmer, but he also worked in a distillery until the day he "got religion" and quit because his conscience told him that liquor was evil and that he should make no contribution to its manufacture. He remained a farmer for the rest of his life. His strong religious feelings were apparently passed on to his son, for Milton joined the United Brethren Church at the age of eighteen. At twenty-two, he was entitled to preach in the church after attending a small college at Hartsville, Indiana. He then went to the Willamette Valley area of Oregon and taught for two years in a small church-sponsored college. There he met Susan Catherine Koerner, a student, and they were married on November 24, 1859.

7

The Milton Wrights returned to Indiana, where Reverend Wright was named minister of a church in Hartsville and was also on the faculty of his alma mater. Their first son, Reuchlin, was born in 1861; Lorin, the second son, was born eighteen months later. Wilbur, the third boy, was born on April 16, 1867, on a small farm near the town of Millsville, Indiana. He was named after Wilbur Fiske, a friend of the Wrights'.

In 1869, Reverend Wright was appointed editor of the United Brethren weekly magazine, *The Religious Telescope*, which required that he move to Dayton, Ohio.

The Reverend purchased a new but modest frame house on the best side of the city. Its address—7 Hawthorne Street—would become the most famous address in aviation history. Orville was born there on August 19, 1871. He was named after Orville Dewey, a minister friend of his father's. On Orville's third birthday, a sister named Katharine was added to the family. None of the Wright children was given a middle name.

Reverend Wright was called by his church to move to Cedar Rapids, Iowa; then Richmond, Indiana; and finally back to Dayton, where the Wrights again settled at 7 Hawthorne Street. The family returned to Dayton a few days before Wilbur would have attended the high school graduation ceremony and received his diploma.

"Should I make the trip back to Richmond to get my diploma?" he asked his family at dinner one evening.

"What do *you* want to do, son?" his father replied.

"It's only fifty miles but it seems like a waste of time

to me just to get a piece of paper. I know I finished high school; you know it and my friends know it. I don't think I'll go." Wilbur spoke quietly as if arriving at the answer to a math problem. His father nodded in assent and the rest of the family agreed with his conclusion. And so, Wilbur Wright never did receive his high school diploma.

Orville had left school at Richmond under different circumstances. He was nearing the end of the sixth grade when his mischievous ways caused his teacher to dismiss him from school. "And you may not return, young man, until your parents come to see me and promise me you'll behave!" she said.

Neither of the Wright parents could see the teacher. Reverend Wright was out of town and Mrs. Wright could not spare the time from packing for the move to Dayton. So Orville simply did not go to school the last several weeks of his sixth grade. In the fall of that year, when he tried to enroll in the seventh grade at Dayton, the principal refused him admittance without proof of having completed the sixth grade. This was one of the few times in his young life that Orville defied his elders. He protested so vehemently and eloquently that the principal agreed to let him into seventh grade classes to see if he could keep up. "If I can't, sir," Orville promised, "you have every right to put me back. But you don't have to worry. I'll show you."

Orville did show the school authorities. He passed the final arithmetic exam that year with the highest mark of any student in Dayton.

But his ability in mathematics was matched by a

playful nature. For almost the rest of his school years, Orville was required to sit in the front row of each class so that the teachers could keep an eye on him.

No one knows what makes an inventor out of a mischievous boy. Perhaps it is a combination of an insatiable curiosity, excellent mechanical ability, and a strong desire to create a machine or a process that will make life easier, do a job better, or perform a feat considered impossible before the invention was made. But there is no doubt that sympathetic and understanding parents also help if the inventor happens to be living at home. And it helps, too, if there are ancestors and relatives who have been inclined to invent things.

Orville and Wilbur Wright had all of these advantages. Their brother Lorin had worked out an improvement on a hay-baling machine, and their mother was always inventing something to make her household chores easier. More often than not, her inventiveness showed itself in her uncanny ability to adapt some normally discarded household item to a new use. Reverend Wright, a good man with tools, had once made a crude typewriter. He would have liked to have spent more time at his workbench but his duties in the church came first and he was often required to travel away from home.

One of the first signs of inventive teamwork shown by the two youngest brothers had occurred when Wilbur was about twelve years old and Orville was eight. They wanted to earn some pocket money and decided that the best way to earn it was to sell junk to Carmody's junkyard. There were many farmers around Dayton who had secondhand metal and wooden articles that Mr. Carmody wanted, but he had no wagon to haul the articles and the farmers usually had no desire to deliver the worthless things to him.

The boys approached Mr. Carmody and asked, "If we bring the junk to you, will you pay us for it?"

"Certainly, lads. And I'll pay you well by the pound. I'll tell you about some of the special things I need and I'll work out a special bonus if you find them and bring them to me."

The boys were delighted, although they had a problem. They needed a wagon but the family could not finance it. They would have to build one that they could pull with a heavy load. While the body was easy to build, the wheels were the problem. Wooden wheels were too heavy; besides, those they could find in Mr. Carmody's junkyard were too badly damaged.

One day Orville found two old tricycles that had been left at the yard and asked Mr. Carmody to let him have them. When the friendly old man consented, Orville rushed home and the two lads worked diligently trying to affix them to the wagon bed. They ran into trouble and in desperation called their mother.

Mrs. Wright took one look and said, "Friction. You've got to get rid of the friction between the axles and the wheels. Remember the grease that farmers put in their wagon-wheel hubs? That's to cut down on friction. Polish the ends of the axles and the insides of those tricycle wheels and put lots of axle grease on them."

This was an important lesson to the two boys and they never forgot it. Overcoming friction is one of man's greatest engineering problems. While it can

11

never be eliminated completely, it can be reduced, and when it is reduced far enough, man can travel faster and engines can work better. The Wright brothers found that the two of them could pull a much greater load with their light wheels when the axles were greased. They calculated that they could haul ten times their combined weight to Carmody's junkyard with their more efficient vehicle. An elementary lesson in mechanics was thoroughly learned by trial and error.

In his early teens Wilbur Wright demonstrated his first bit of inventiveness. He had obtained a contract to fold the eight-page church paper each week. It was a monotonous chore and Wilbur soon detested it. But instead of quitting, he quietly analyzed his own feelings about the task. He told himself that the real reason he hated the job was because it was too boring and took too long. Could it be done faster and with less manual effort on his part? It was not long before he invented a simple folding machine that he operated with a foot treadle taken from an old sewing machine. From then on the tedious job became fun because he had cut the work time in half, and had experienced the joy of creating with his own mind and hands.

As far as Wilbur was concerned, the secret of his invention had really been given to him by his mother. She designed all her own clothes but first made a sketch of what she thought she wanted to make. Then she translated the sketch into paper patterns, and before she ever put the scissors to a piece of cloth, she tested the pattern on herself for size. "Make your mistakes on paper if you can," she told her children, "and it will save you grief later." Wilbur had remembered this advice and had made rough sketches of his folding machine before he looked for his materials. It was another lesson well learned at an early age.

While the two youngest Wright brothers collaborated on many projects around the home, the four years' difference in their ages often led them along separate paths. At the age of twelve, Orville became interested in printing and teamed up with a boyhood friend named Ed Sines, who had a small printing press. They set up shop, first in the Sineses' kitchen and then in a small room at the Wrights' home, and called themselves "Messrs. Sines and Wright."

One of their first ideas was to publish and sell a newspaper to their classmates. They called it *The Midget* because it was only three by four-and-a-half inches in size—the limitation caused by the size of their printing press bed. The paper lasted for one issue, mainly because Reverend Wright would not let them distribute it. It was a four-page paper but they had printed nothing on the third page except "Sines and Wright."

"Your readers will think you are lazy," the Reverend told the boys, "and they'll never buy the second issue. Besides, I don't think you boys spent much time writing your copy before you set it in type, did you?"

Orville and Ed had to admit that they had composed their articles as they went along. But this setback did not deter them. They took orders for handbills from local merchants and made a little spending money while gaining good business experience. Ed Sines eventually lost interest in the project, but Orville did not. He bought a bigger press and took on larger printing orders. During two summer vacations he took a job with a Dayton printer and decided that what he really needed for his own printing business was a still larger press. He could not afford to buy one. Could he build one? He decided to try.

The job was not easy, and he finally asked Wilbur to help him. The two of them, using the cut-and-try method after first making preliminary drawings, constructed a unique press which Wilbur said could print a small newspaper if they wanted it to.

The idea stuck with Orville and he decided that he would start a weekly neighborhood newspaper to be called the *West Side News.* The first issue was dated March 1, 1889, in which Orville proudly announced: "This week we issue the first number of the *West Side News,* a paper to be published in the interests of the people and business institutions of the West Side. Whatever tends to their advancement, moral, mental, and financial, will receive our closest attention."

Ed Sines became the business manager and sold ads. Wilbur, fascinated by the immediate success of the paper, helped out in the shop and then wrote some humorous editorials. Orville added Wilbur's name to the masthead as "editor," and listed himself as "publisher."

The *West Side News* was launched during Orville's senior year in high school. Disinterested in his studies because the curriculum seemed to be nothing but a review of the previous years, he enrolled as a special Latin student and attended school only an hour or so each day. His intention was to qualify for college entrance examinations, and he knew that he was deficient in Latin. He just did not worry about the other subjects. As a result, he did not qualify for his high school diploma and, like his brother Wilbur, never did officially graduate from high school.

The *West Side News* prospered, and Orville decided not to go to college. In April, 1890, the weekly *West Side News* became a daily under the new title of *The Evening Item*. This venture lasted about four months, although four years later the Wrights were again publishing a neighborhood weekly called *Snapshots*.

In the interim the two brothers, by now used to working together, became interested in bicycles. New ones with pneumatic tires had been imported from Europe and immediately became popular. Orville purchased one and took up racing for the fun of it. The two of them, noting how much interest there was in the new sport, decided to enter the business of selling and repairing bicycles. They rented a shop and the venture was so successful from the time they started in December, 1892, that within the next two years they had to move three times to larger quarters.

Selling and repairing gave them the opportunity to learn the strengths and weaknesses of a dozen or more types of the foreign bicycles. The only logical next step was to improve on these models and sell the domestic ones for less than the imported models—if they could. They could and they did. Their first model was named "the Van Cleve." It was followed by "the St. Clair," and then by "the Wright Special," which sold for only eighteen dollars as compared to about one hundred dollars for imported British bikes. Furthermore, they guaranteed buyers free service for a year—an unprecedented offer.

The continued success of the bicycle business gave the brothers a comfortable income (especially since they were not married and continued to live at home) and an opportunity to experiment. Orville designed and built a calculating machine that could add and multiply, and a typewriter which was an improvement over those then available. Wilbur experimented with gears and sprockets.

Working closely day after day, the two brothers had become almost inseparable. Wilbur's health had been impaired as the result of a skating accident in which he lost all of his upper front teeth. He also suffered from a heart disorder, and this combination tended to make him less active and less communicative than Orville. The loss of their mother in 1889 seemed to bring them closer together than ever. Their similar interests and corresponding curiosity, persistence, and mechanical aptitude made them an ideal team, and seemed to fit them for something bigger in life than making and repairing bicycles. However, neither their family nor their friends would have dreamed that these two tinkerers would one day be world famous. Fame certainly seemed even less assured when the two men, now in their twenties, became interested in kites and then gliders. It was the consensus in West Dayton that "those Wright boys are going to kill themselves one of these days!"

CHAPTER III

The Glider Experiments

NO one has ever ascertained exactly when the Wright brothers first thought of flight. They recalled being fascinated by a toy, called a "helicopter," which their father had given them in 1878. They were living in Cedar Rapids at the time and both remembered being intrigued with the fact that this small toy had two "air-screws" under rubber-band tension rotating in opposite directions, which enabled the toy to rise and fly around the room until the rubber band was untwisted. They used this principle, consciously or unconsciously, many years later when they designed the first airplane and equipped it with two propellers rotating in opposite directions.

The Wrights made a number of copies of their "helicopter" and all of them flew successfully. However, when they tried to build a larger one, it would not get off the ground. They did not know why at the time, so they lost interest.

In 1896 the Wrights first became interested in gliding. They had read of the gliding experiments conducted in Germany that year by Otto Lilienthal. Their interest increased when Lilienthal was killed while attempting a long glide off a high hill near Stoellen. They felt, and historians now agree, that Lilienthal had come closer to solving the mystery of controlled flight than anyone else up to that time. Lilienthal's preoccupation with flight had come about by studying the flight of birds. He tried to imitate them, and the conclusions he reached as the result of his own experiments were published after his death under the title of *Der Vogelflug als Grundlage der Fliegerkunst* ("Bird Flight as the Basis of the Flying Art") .

The Wrights were intrigued by the very idea of flying like a bird, and they sought out everything written on the subject. In 1899 their interest was again aroused by a book on ornithology (the study of birds) , and it was then that they decided to try gliding for themselves. Orville recalled their reasoning many years later. "We could not understand that there was anything about a bird that would enable it to fly that could not be built on a larger scale and used by man. At this time our thought pertained more particularly to gliding flight and soaring. If the bird's wings would sustain it in the air without the use of any muscular effort, we did not see why man could not be sustained by the same means." *

Wilbur wrote a letter to the Smithsonian Institution in Washington, D.C., because the Smithsonian had

* Orville Wright, *How We Invented the Airplane* (New York, David McKay, 1953), p. 19.

18

sponsored much research on the subject of flight. He asked for any publications that could be furnished. For the first time the Wrights learned of the writings of Samuel P. Langley, Octave Chanute, and many other experimenters. They were much impressed with the caliber of men who had also sought to solve the problems of flight: Leonardo da Vinci; Sir George Cayley, one of the first inventors of the internal combustion engine; Alexander Graham Bell, inventor of the telephone; and Thomas A. Edison. They also learned that the whole subject of controlled flight was fast becoming a topic of public ridicule because a number of other men of lesser scientific ability had tried and failed so miserably. "Flying is as impossible to achieve as perpetual motion," many said. The Wrights were not so sure about this, especially when they found that Lilienthal had made so many successful flights before his death and had had a total of about five hours in the air.

The Wrights reasoned that the failures of earlier experimenters were due primarily to their inability to properly balance their gliders in flight. Most, if not all, had tried to maintain equilibrium in the air merely by shifting their bodies from side to side or backward and forward, as on a seesaw. To overcome this difficulty, the first method that the Wrights thought of was to construct two separate wings connected by gears to a center shaft, so that one wing could turn upward when the other turned downward. They gave up this idea when they could not figure out any way to construct a framework that would be light yet strong enough.

In the spring of 1899, Wilbur was struck with an inspiration that was to prove most significant in their search for the secret of control. Orville described how Wilbur told him about it:

"One evening when I returned home . . . Wilbur showed me a method of getting the same results as we had contemplated in our first idea without the structural defects of the original. He demonstrated the method by means of a small pasteboard box, which had . . . the opposite ends removed. By holding the top forward corner and the rear lower corner of one end of the box between his thumb and forefinger and the rear upper corner and the lower forward corner of the other end of the box in the like manner, and by pressing the corners together, the upper and lower surface of the box were given a helicoidal [spiral] twist, presenting the top and bottom surfaces of the box at different angles on the right and left sides." *

Wilbur had stumbled on the idea of wing warping, and his enthusiasm carried Orville with him. To try the idea, the two brothers constructed a kite which looked more like a model glider. It had two wings measuring five feet from tip to tip and thirteen inches wide, mounted one above the other. They connected strings to the corners of the wing tips and ran them to short sticks held by the operator, much as powered model airplanes are "flown" today. With a stick in each hand, the operator could twist the wings and cause the wing surfaces to be exposed to the wind at varying angles. This change in angle would increase or decrease the lift under a wing and cause the kite to turn.

* *How We Invented the Airplane,* pp. 22–23.

In addition to the wing warping arrangement, the Wrights added an additional structure to the rear of the kite to help stabilize it in flight. They connected it in such a way that when the wings were warped, the structure helped to turn the kite in the same direction that the wings were turning—thus helping to stabilize the craft. They had invented both the aileron and the elevator, which are the basic aerodynamic surfaces by which all airplanes are controlled today.

The initial successes of their controllable kite inspired the men from Dayton, and they began a serious study of all the literature then available on the science of flight. They were appalled at the loss of life and financial disasters suffered by those who had previously attempted to fly, particularly balloonists. They understood more clearly than ever the difficulty of the problem they were trying to solve. As they read about earlier failures, they could not be convinced in their own minds that their predecessors had the right approach.

"We could not help thinking," Wilbur reflected later, "that many of their troubles might have been avoided and that others might have been overcome by the adoption of more adequate methods." *

The death of Otto Lilienthal had left Octave Chanute as the foremost living authority on gliders. A successful railroad engineer and bridge builder, he had turned to aeronautics and begun the construction of gliders, using the same principles in wing construction as he had used in bridge trusses. At the age of sixty-four, he took up gliding himself and made about two

* *The Aeronautical Journal* (London, 1916), p. 118.

thousand glides from 1896 to 1898. He built several types of gliders but focused on the biplane type because it proved most successful. When the Wrights found that its design explained their own successes, they decided to contact Chanute by letter. From the time of that first letter, written by Wilbur in May, 1900, Chanute became a firm friend and confidant of the Wright brothers. Wilbur described their hopes, plans, and theories so earnestly that Chanute was deeply impressed and resolved to help them.

In his first letter, Wilbur asked Chanute for information as to the best place in the United States to conduct experiments with a man-carrying glider. Chanute suggested locations in Florida and California, but added that even better locations might be found along the coastal areas of Georgia and the Carolinas. Since the latter areas were closer to Dayton, the Wrights contacted the United States Weather Bureau and learned that a place near one of the weather reporting stations might be suitable. The spot had an odd name: Kitty Hawk, North Carolina.

Wilbur immediately wrote to the man in charge of the Kitty Hawk station asking for information about the locality, its terrain, and other details, in addition to weather information. Joseph J. Dosher, observer-in-charge, replied matter-of-factly, and gave Wilbur's letter to the postmaster, William J. Tate. No one knows what motivated Tate to reply also, but he wrote in such splendid detail that the Wrights decided on Kitty Hawk as the place for their experiments, sight unseen. Throughout the summer of 1900, they constructed their first man-carrying glider. In September, Wilbur set out for Kitty Hawk while Orville stayed behind to tend to the bicycle shop. When Wilbur was ready for his brother to join him, he would send a telegram.

Wilbur was not exactly prepared for what he found when he finally arrived at his destination. He had expected the area to be isolated but not so desolate. There were miles of sand dunes, with only occasional patches of beach grass bending in the constant wind. The only man-made structures along the beach were the Kitty Hawk lifesaving station and a small shack beside it which housed the weather bureau's recording equipment. The tiny hamlet of Kitty Hawk, consisting of about a dozen widely scattered houses, was located about a mile back from the ocean. Four miles to the south was the Kill Devil lifesaving station. Wilbur surveyed the area and decided to pitch their tent on a site about a mile south of the nearest house in Kitty Hawk. He stayed at the Tate home until after Orville arrived about three weeks later.

Once the brothers had their equipment stowed in the tent and the glider assembled, they waited for good weather. Mr. Dosher had told them that the winds at Kitty Hawk averaged about fifteen miles an hour during the fall months. He was right, but the Wright brothers learned that averages can be deceiving. Just as a stream can have an average depth of three feet, yet be thirty feet deep in the center, the winds at Kitty Hawk could reach sixty miles an hour on one day and be completely calm the next. They had calculated that they would need a wind of between seventeen and twenty-two miles per hour to sustain their glider with one of them aboard. More wind was needed, however, to get it off the ground in the first place.

It was soon obvious that much time would be lost if they waited for winds of exactly the right speeds to lift them off the ground. So they decided to fly their contraption as a kite, with bicycle chains for weights, whenever the wind was too low. They manipulated the controls from the ground by the use of cords.

The brothers spent most of their time flying the machine as a kite during their first stay at Kitty Hawk. However, just before returning to Dayton, they made about a dozen glides for a total of only two minutes of flying time. These experiments marked the first time that anyone had flown a glider while lying prone on the lower wing. It was a significant change from the attempts of others who had always tried to glide while in a sitting position. To the Wrights, their own reasoning was simple. A man sitting up offered too much resistance to the wind—five times as much as a man lying down, they calculated. As Wilbur explained later, the horizontal position was better because "only one square foot instead of five would be exposed."

When the two brothers packed their gear for the trip home, they were happy with the results they had obtained. The control mechanism had worked better than they had expected. Now they were sure they were on the right track, and resolved that they would return the next year with a larger glider built along the same lines but with more lifting surface on the wings.

The next months were full of intense activity for the Wrights. They wrote to Octave Chanute and told him in great detail of their findings at Kitty Hawk. Chanute was as delighted with their success as they were and answered promptly. Could he quote them in an article he was writing for *Cassier's Magazine*? If so, how should their names be mentioned?

Both Wilbur and Orville were pleased that the famous Chanute wanted to recognize their work, but they decided that it was much too soon to give the public a full account of their flights. Chanute could say that they had made several glides, if he wanted to, and he could refer to them as "Messrs. Wilbur and Orville Wright."

Chanute understood their reluctance to reveal their theories, because much more experimentation was necessary. He was intrigued, however, with the fact that these two bicycle repairmen, operating completely on their own resources, seemed closer than all the others to discovering the secret of flight. He intimated that he would like to meet the Wrights. Could it be arranged?

The brothers were flabbergasted. Of course the great Chanute could see them and also inspect the new glider that they were making. At the same time, they were filled with dread. Chanute was a distinguished engineer. Suppose he came all the way to Dayton, took one look, and knew from his own engineering experience that their larger glider would not fly. The fear of failure spurred them on. The famous Chanute, bearded and white-haired, arrived at 7 Hawthorne Street in June, 1901.

The rapport established between this man of the world and the two unknown bicycle mechanics was immediate and long-lasting. They discussed all the previous great men who had experimented with flight and had eventually given up. Did the Wrights think they could succeed when so many others had failed?

"We don't know, Mr. Chanute," Wilbur replied, "but we believe that all the others spent too much time *thinking* about flying and not enough time *trying* to fly."

Orville agreed and used the analogy of learning to ride a horse. "There are two ways," he said. "One is to get into the saddle and try until you've mastered it. The other is to sit on the fence and watch, and then go into the house, take out pencil and paper, and analyze how best to avoid getting thrown off. The latter way is safer but the former method turns out the best riders."

Chanute was impressed with the attitude of these two young men. They obviously had the personal courage to carry out their experiments and were perfectly willing to risk their necks. But how about finances? How much did their first glider cost?

"About fifteen dollars," Wilbur answered, "but the one we're building now will cost much more."

"Do you have anyone contributing money to help you?" asked Chanute.

"No, sir," Orville answered. "And we don't want any outside financial help. We will bear the costs ourselves. If we fail, then no one else will be sorry but us."

"But surely you hope to make money from your machine if you succeed, don't you?" the older man asked.

Wilbur thought a moment and then made the most inaccurate prediction of his life. "It is foolish to think of making money from building a flying machine," he said. "No one could ever earn a living from it. We will make our living from bicycles—not gliders or flying machines."

Chanute became more impressed by these young men with each passing minute. When they showed him their new glider, which was still under construction, he was amazed at the engineering cleverness displayed by the unschooled, self-taught mechanics. He felt that of all the men in history who had tried before, the Wright brothers could very well be the ones to find the key. He resolved to help them if he could.

Encouraged by Chanute's interest, the Wrights returned to Kitty Hawk in July, 1901. Chanute had arranged for two of his friends to join them: George Spratt, a man with some soaring experience and medical training; and E. C. Huffaker, who was building a glider for Chanute.

The new Wright glider had the same general design and control system as the first one but was much larger. The wing span was now 22 feet and the wing area had been increased from 165 square feet to 290. Its weight had increased from 52 to 98 pounds. The size of the front elevator had increased correspondingly.

Since more wind was needed for the larger glider than for the original one, the four men took the machine farther down the beach to Kill Devil Hill for its first trial. After a great deal of checking, which made Spratt and Huffaker impatient, the Wrights finally allowed their machine to take to the air. After a number of short flights, a glide of 315 feet was made in 19 seconds—the longest flight yet. Several more flights were made that day, all of which covered more ground and were of longer duration than those of the year before.

However, the Wrights were disappointed. The glider did not handle as easily and smoothly as before. What was wrong?

Wilbur was the first to find out the hard way. On one flight he rose to about twenty feet off the ground and was gliding nicely forward when, without warning, the craft nosed downward suddenly and plowed into the sand. Luckily Wilbur was unhurt, but the mystery of the craft's performance stunned him. "That was exactly the way Otto Lilienthal was killed," he said, brushing the sand out of his clothes. "We've got to find out what happened!"

As he had promised when he saw them last, Octave Chanute visited Kitty Hawk in August, 1901, and listened carefully as the Wrights reasoned out their difficulty. The three men concluded that since the lift of the new machine was only about one-third of what their calculations said it should be, perhaps their calculations were wrong. Chanute asked what tables of air pressures they had used.

"We used Lilienthal's tables," Wilbur replied.

There was silence for a moment, and then Orville said what they had all just thought. "Yes, and Lilienthal is dead—because he used his own tables and they must have been wrong!"

The sudden realization that they had based all their calculations of wing size, camber, and angle of incidence on incorrect tables plunged both of the Wrights into deep despair. Chanute recognized this and begged them not to be discouraged. "You have already flown farther than anyone else in the world even if your calculations are wrong. Please do not quit now!"

The Wrights did not quit, although they felt it useless to continue their current experiments with that machine. After Chanute left, they made two more world-record glides of 366 and 389 feet, but these did not please them. The flights were not under full control and they knew it. One of them might be killed or injured if they kept trying to fly higher and farther. They packed up on August 22, and left Kitty Hawk. They thought they would never return.

In the following weeks, as the Wrights plunged back into the bicycle business, they received several letters from Chanute encouraging them to go on with their gliding experiments. Then one day Chanute wrote to ask Wilbur to speak to the Western Society of Engineers in Chicago about their work at Kitty Hawk. It was only because of their friendship for Chanute that Wilbur consented to make the address.

In composing his speech, Wilbur stated that the air pressure tables upon which they had based their glider design were in error. Since most of the scientific world had accepted them, the statement was a bold one for an unknown to make. Orville was worried that they would both be ridiculed if the tables proved right and their application of them proved wrong.

As a result, Orville constructed a wind tunnel so that he could measure in miniature the difference in pressures that curved wing surfaces made as compared to flat surfaces of equal area. The results were not conclusive, but there was enough difference between Lilienthal's tables and theirs to cause the Wrights to believe that they were correct. However, Wilbur toned down his speech considerably, and the two brothers decided to do more wind tunnel experiments after Wilbur's return from Chicago.

The fall and winter of 1901–2 were largely spent constructing a new and bigger wind tunnel. It was a box six feet long; air was driven in one end by a one-cylinder gasoline engine hooked to a fan. The air passed through a crosshatch of holes to even the flow, and over a sample wing section suspended against the air. The brothers used an ingenious arrangement of wire and old hacksaw blades to measure the results.

The Wrights tested over two hundred different types of wing surfaces in as many combinations as they could think of. They used single-wing models, bi-wing, and even tri-wing configurations. Thick and thin wings were tested, along with many different combinations of wing span and wing width. Carefully noting the results, they arrived at some interesting and startling conclusions. Their box of wind was leading them nearer to the truth than anyone had ever been. Their excitement grew as they compiled their findings into neat tables of figures. However, they were forced to stop their work, because their business was beginning to suffer.

Wilbur sent copies of the new tables to Chanute, and explained how they had developed them. He also said that they wished they could have continued their wind tunnel tests but that they had set an arbitrary date to stop, and they did.

Chanute was more than ever convinced that the Wrights were on the brink of discovery. He knew a man—Andrew Carnegie—whom he felt could be easily persuaded to support such promising research. Would they accept a gift of ten thousand dollars from him to continue their work if it could be arranged?

The Wrights agonized over their answer for days. Taking the money would make them feel an obligation to the donor to devote full time to their experiments. The Wright Cycle Company, in spite of the time they devoted to their experiments, was supporting them adequately. It would not be fair to either the business or the donor to try to do both.

Wilbur finally replied to Chanute. "I do not think it would be wise for me to accept help in carrying our present tests further . . ." But they promised to continue their tests, and when warm weather came, they had built a new glider based on the new tables. In August, 1902, they returned to Kitty Hawk.

Kitty Hawk had not changed, but the Wright brothers' attitude had, since they had left the sand dunes the year before. The shack they had constructed was still standing but in bad shape. They repaired it and built an addition to afford more space for themselves and their new glider.

The glider was even larger this time—thirty-two feet from wing tip to wing tip. It had twin rudders in the rear and the control system had been changed. On September 19, it was ready to fly.

It had been the Wrights' custom to fly the glider first as a kite, with no pilot aboard. They did this for three hours, and it handled so well that they decided to fly it themselves. Trying short flights at not more than six feet from the ground, and always with someone holding the wings, they made about twenty-five flights. The craft handled superbly, but the true tests were yet to come. They would have to try it in greater winds, from a higher hill, and without anyone holding on to prevent accidents.

The brothers moved to Kill Devil Hill but the flights were sometimes disappointing. On several occasions, both pilots lost control and dug a wing into the sand—well-digging, they called it. Something was still wrong. Both pilots had warped the wings as far as they would go but they could not keep the wing from striking the sand.

After a great deal of thought, Orville had a flash of inspiration. He decided that the trouble was not in the wings but in the tail they had added. "It's got to be a movable surface instead of fixed!" he shouted one night. "When a wing goes down, a movable tail could help bring it back to regain balance!"

Wilbur agreed that the idea made sense, and the two men rigged the rudder wires to the same controls that warped the wing surfaces. Instead of a double, fixed tail, they constructed a single, movable rudder. Wilbur was the first to try it, and he was elated. Chanute, who had just arrived to test a new tri-winged glider made just for him, was astonished at the ease with which the Wright machine soared. His own machine, he quickly found out, was unsuccessful.

After Chanute left, the Wrights made more than one thousand glides in their final ten days at Kitty Hawk. In the last two days alone, their records show that they made almost two hundred and fifty flights, several of them more than six hundred feet, and into a thirty-six-mile wind. The longest flight lasted twenty-six seconds.

The Wrights left Kitty Hawk in October, 1902, broke, but in the highest spirits they had ever known. They had set a number of world records. They had each made more flights in a controllable glider than anyone else. They had proven that their tables were more accurate than those previously accepted as infallible. They had solved the mystery of balance and control.

"There's only one thing left for us to do now," Orville said as they took the train to Dayton.

"What's that?" Wilbur asked.

"Put a motor on it," Orville replied, "so we can stay up longer."

Wilbur nodded in agreement. He had already been thinking the same thing.

CHAPTER IV

The First to Fly

❧ ❧ ❧ ❧

THE idea of putting an engine on their controllable glider grew into an obsession, now that the Wrights felt they had proven the accuracy of their laboratory wind tunnel experiments by actual flight. If an engine were to be mounted on the glider frame, what kind of engine should it be—steam or gasoline-powered? How should propellers be designed to pull the craft through the air? How heavy could the machine be and still carry itself and a pilot aloft? There were many other questions to be answered before their dream could be realized.

Since the engine was the most important problem to be solved, work began on it as soon as the brothers returned to Dayton in 1902. They quickly decided against the steam engine as being too bulky and complicated. The gasoline engine would be simpler and lighter.

Although the Wrights had actually designed and

built a one-cylinder, air-cooled engine to operate some of the tools in their bicycle shop, they did not feel competent enough to build one of the size and power that they needed. By careful calculation, they figured that the glider engine had to produce at least eight horsepower and could not weigh more than two hundred pounds.

If they could not build one themselves, the only solution was to contact all the companies making the new gasoline-powered automobiles to see if someone could design an engine to their specifications. To their surprise, most of the companies declined to even consider the idea of furnishing an engine for this purpose. So the Wrights discovered that if they were going to have an engine at all, they would have to build it themselves.

The two brothers did not just go out to their shop and start tinkering. As was their pattern of operation, they debated for hours in the family kitchen and labored over drawings and figures for days before agreeing on the design and the method to proceed. Fortunately, they had an employee in their shop who was a metalsmith, and he had proved adept at converting the Wright drawings of bicycle parts into hardware. Charley Taylor had only three power tools—a lathe, bandsaw, and drill—but the products he turned out were always the work of a craftsman. Taylor was thirty-three years old, quiet, dedicated, and the possessor of a pair of keen, blue eyes and a scraggly moustache.

The Wrights made detailed drawings of the four-cylinder, water-cooled engine as they visualized it.

The cylinders were to be four inches in diameter and have a four-inch stroke. Could Charley make a test engine based on these drawings?

Taylor quietly put down his tools, slowly adjusted his glasses, and leaned over the workbench to study this latest of the Wright brainstorms. After a few minutes he looked up, shrugged, and pinned the drawings along the wall over his bench. In about two weeks he had a test model, which he had built without a lubrication system and had hooked up to the natural gas supply which ran their small shop engine. To lubricate the parts after starting, Charley merely "painted" the moving parts with a brush dripping with oil.

This first primitive step with a small test engine was so successful that the Wrights authorized Charley to build them one they could attach to their new glider. He immediately set to work locating a cast-aluminum block and drilling the required holes. The cylinders and pistons were cast iron. Other parts were fashioned of available materials adapted to his needs. The result was an engine that weighed only one hundred and seventy pounds with all accessories attached, and developed twelve horsepower.

While Charley was working patiently on the engine, the brothers worked on what proved to be a more difficult problem—the propellers. They first studied boat propellers and were surprised to learn that marine-engine manufacturers were still using the "cut-and-try" method of designing propellers. Again they decided that they could not rely on anyone else, and had to experiment and design their own.

The Wrights, after much debate between them, concluded that the propellers had to cut through the air just as the wings did. Therefore, they reasoned that propellers had to be airfoils just as wings were. But, in addition, propellers had to be slightly twisted so that they could pull the craft through the air much as a screw works its way into a piece of wood.

The road to agreement had not been easy. To anyone listening to them argue, it seemed likely that they were going to come to blows, but they never did. Oddly enough, as Orville recalled years later, "after an hour or so of heated argument, we would discover that we were as far from agreement as when we started, but that each had changed to the other's original position."

The brotherly debate proved fruitful and they decided that they had to use two propellers rotating in opposite directions. These would be hooked up to Charley Taylor's engine by bicycle chains running over sprockets exactly as on a bike.

It took the Wrights months to arrive at the point where the glider, engine, propellers, and the required gears were ready to be packed for another trip to Kitty Hawk. They arrived there in late September, and after a few days spent in setting up camp and erecting a building that would partially house their machine, they began the tedious work of assembling the craft. This took three weeks, but for relief they brought out the 1902 glider that they had left behind and practiced flying it.

The new glider assembly went smoothly but engine problems quickly developed. The propeller shafts proved not to be strong enough and were sent back to

Charley Taylor in Dayton for reworking. Then sprocket problems developed, and by the time these were solved and Charley had sent new propeller shafts, bad weather had set in. Freezing rain, snow, and heavy winds kept them inside. But the time was well spent designing a mechanism which would embody three important factors: the number of engine revolutions made during a flight; the distance traveled through the air; and the exact time in seconds of any flight. Thus, an engine revolution counter, an anemometer, and a stopwatch were ingeniously connected, which would start when the machine left the ground and shut off automatically when it came to a stop.

When the weather cleared at the end of November, new troubles developed. One of Taylor's newly fashioned tubular shafts showed a bad crack. The only solution was for Orville to take it back to Dayton, explain the problem to Charley, and return.

Orville returned on December 11, but it was December 14 before the machine and the weather were in accord. With the help of five men from the nearby Kill Devil lifesaving station, the Wrights pulled the 750-pound machine to the monorail launching apparatus they had designed. A coin was flipped, and Wilbur won the chance to be the first man to try their flying machine.

The engine was started and warmed up. When everything seemed to be in order, Wilbur climbed aboard and stretched out prone, his head forward. Orville got on one wing tip to balance the machine as it started down the monorail. When Wilbur gave the signal, the restraining wire was dropped and the machine leaped

forward with a roar. After a run of only about forty
feet, it lifted from the rail, climbed a few feet, stalled
and plunged, left wing first, into the sand at the foot
of the hill. One of the skids dragged and snapped and
several other wooden parts were split. Wilbur had
been in the air $3\frac{1}{2}$ seconds and had been airborne for
a distance of 105 feet. Neither of the brothers considered this a successful flight and never counted it as
such in later years. They dragged the machine back
to the shed, repaired the broken parts, and were ready
to try again on the morning of December 17. Orville
Wright described that historic day in his typical mat-
ter-of-fact style:

"When we arose on the morning of the 17th, the
puddles of water, which had been standing about the
camp since the recent rains, were covered with ice. The
wind had a velocity of 10 to 12 meters per second (22
to 27 miles an hour). We thought it would die down
before long, and so remained indoors the early part of
the morning. But when ten o'clock arrived, and the
wind was as brisk as ever, we decided that we had
better get the machine out and attempt a flight. We
hung out the signal for the men of the Life Saving
Station. We thought that by facing the flyer into a
strong wind, there ought to be no trouble in launching
it from the level ground about camp. We realized the
difficulties of flying in so high a wind, but estimated
that the added dangers in flight would be partly com-
pensated for by the slower speed in landing.

"We laid the track on a smooth stretch of ground
about 100 feet west of the new building. The biting
cold wind made work difficult, and we had to warm up

frequently in our living room, where we had a good fire in an improvised stove made of a large carbide can. By the time all was ready, J. T. Daniels, W. S. Dough, and A. D. Etheridge, members of the Kill Devil Life Saving Station; W. C. Brinkley of Manteo; and Johnny Moore, a boy from Nag's Head, had arrived.

"Wilbur having used his turn in the unsuccessful attempt on the 14th, the right to the first trial now belonged to me. After running the motor a few minutes to heat it up, I released the wire that held the machine to the track, and the machine started forward into the wind. Wilbur ran at the side of the machine, holding the wing to balance it on the track. Unlike the start on the 14th, made in a calm, the machine, facing a 27-mile wind, started very slowly. Wilbur was able to stay with it till it lifted from the track after a 40-foot run. One of the Life Saving men snapped the camera for us, taking a picture just as the machine had reached the end of the track and had risen to a height of about 2 feet. The slow forward speed of the machine over the ground is clearly shown in the picture by Wilbur's attitude. He stayed along beside the machine without any effort.

"The course of the flight up and down was exceedingly erratic, partly due to the irregularity of the air and partly to the lack of experience in handling this machine. The control of the front rudder was difficult on account of its being balanced too near the center. This gave it a tendency to turn itself when started, so that it turned too far on one side and then too far on the other. As a result, the machine would rise suddenly to about 10 feet, and then as suddenly dart for the

WRIGHT CYCLE COMPANY

1127 WEST THIRD STREET

DAYTON. OHIO

ESTABLISHED IN
1892

October 9th, 1905.

The Honorable Secretary of War,

Washington, D. C.

Dear Sir:

Some months ago we made an informal offer to furnish to the War Department practical flying machines suitable for scouting purposes. The matter was referred to the Board of Ordnance and Fortification, which seems to have given it scant consideration. We do not wish to take this invention abroad, unless we find it necessary to do so, and therefore write again, renewing the offer.

We are prepared to furnish a machine on contract, to be accepted only after trial trips in which the conditions of the contract have been fulfilled; the machine to carry an operator and supplies of fuel, etc., sufficient for a flight of one hundred miles; the price of the machine to be regulated according to a sliding scale based on the performance of the machine in the trial trips; the minimum performance to be a flight of at least twenty-five miles at a speed of not less than thirty miles an hour.

We are also willing to take contracts to build machines carrying more than one man.

Respectfully yours,

Letter from Wright brothers to Secretary of War regarding flying machines (All photographs courtesy U. S. Air Force)

The "daddy" of flight, Wright brothers' Model B, first mass production plane ever built, 1911

Wright glider, Kitty Hawk, North Carolina, 1911

Accident with Orville Wright aboard, Kitty Hawk, North Carolina, 1911

Model "CH" Multiple Step Pontoons, 1913

Model "L" sixty horsepower, six-cylinder engine, 1916

Kill Devill Hills N.C.

November 4th 1928.

To Whom it may concern.

This is to certify that W.S.Dough, A.D.Etheridge,and John Moore who are all three eye witnesses of the first flight made by Orville Wright at Kill Devil Hills on December the 17th 1903,assembled at Kill Devil Hills on this date at the request of W.J.Tate (acting for The National Aeronautical Association) for the purpose of agreeing upon and marking for the said Association,the spot where the Wrights Aeroplane first began to move along the ground when this first flight was made.

We understand that this was required so as to enable The Association to erect a memorial upon the place where the first flight actually began,and to prevent the possibility of any future dispute as to the right location.

Beginning with the site of the building which housed The Wrights Plane at the time, distinctly remembering the wind direction at the time,and that the track was laid directly in the wind,coroborating our memory on these facts by the records of the Weather Bureau, remembering that We helped bring the machine from the building and placed it on the track, refering to distances laid down in feet in Orville Wrights article"How We made our first flight" We proceeded to agree upon the spot,and We individually and collectively state without the least mental reservation,that the spot We located is as near correct as it is humanly possible to be with the data in hand to work from after a lapse of twenty five years. We marked the spot with a copper pipe driven into the ground.

We further state,that W.S.Dough, A.D.Etheridge and John Moore are the only persons living who were present on Dec 17th 1903 when Orville Wright made that first flight,except J.T.Daniels(who resides in Edenton N.C.) and Who it was impossible to have present at the time,and Orville Wright Himself.

Respectfully submitted.

Attest *[signature]*

Acting for the
National Aeronautic
Association.

[signature] ------------------------(Seal)

[signature] --------------------------(Seal)

[signature] ----(Seal)

Affidavit as to first Wright flight, Kitty Hawk, North Carolina

Wright Memorial Monument atop Kill Devil Hill, North Carolina

ground. A sudden dart when a little over 100 feet from the end of the track, or a little over 120 feet from the point at which it rose into the air, ended the flight. As the veloc of the wind was over 35 feet per second and the speed of the machine over the ground against this wind 10 feet per second, the speed of the machine relative to the air was over 45 feet per second, and the length of the flight was equivalent to a flight of 540 feet made in calm air.

"This flight lasted only twelve seconds, but it was nevertheless the first in the history of the world in which a machine carrying a man had raised itself by its own power into the air in full flight, had sailed forward without reduction of speed, and had finally landed at a point as high as that from which it started.

"With the assistance of our visitors we carried the machine back to the track and prepared for another flight. The wind, however, had chilled us through, so that before attempting a second flight, we all went to the building again to warm up.

"At twenty minutes after eleven Wilbur started on the second flight. The course of the flight was very much like that of the first, very much up and down. The speed over the ground was somewhat faster than that of the first flight, due to the lesser wind. The duration of the flight was less than a second longer than the first, but the distance covered was about 75 feet greater.

"Twenty minutes later, the third flight started. This one was steadier than the first one an hour before. I was proceeding along pretty well when a sudden gust from the right lifted the machine up 12 to 15 feet and turned it sidewise in an alarming manner. It began a lively

sliding off to the left. I warped the wings to try to re-
cover the lateral balance and at the same time pointed
the machine down to reach the ground as quickly as
possible. The lateral control was more effective than I
had imagined and before I reached the ground the right
wing was lower than the left and struck first. The time
of this flight was 15 seconds and the distance over the
ground a little over 200 feet.

"Wilbur started the fourth and last flight at just 12
o'clock. The first few hundred feet were up and down,
as before, but by the time three hundred feet had been
covered, the machine was under much better control.
The course set for the next four or five hundred feet had
but little undulation. However, when out about eight
hundred feet the machine began pitching again, and,
in one of its darts downward, struck the ground. The
distance over the ground was measured and found to
be 852 feet; the time of flight 59 seconds. The frame
supporting the front rudder was badly broken, but the
main part of the machine was not injured at all. We
estimated that the machine could be put in condition
for flight again in a day or two.

"While we were standing about discussing this last
flight, a sudden strong gust of wind struck the machine
and began to turn it over. Everybody made a rush for
it. Wilbur, who was at one end, seized it in front. Mr.
Daniels and I, who were behind, tried to stop it by holding to the rear uprights.

"All our efforts were in vain. The machine rolled
over and over. Daniels, who had retained his grip, was
carried along with it, and was thrown about, head over
heels, inside of the machine. Fortunately he was not

seriously injured, though badly bruised in falling about against the motor, chain guides, etc. The ribs in the surfaces of the machine were broken, the motor injured, and the chain guides badly bent, so that all possibility of further flights with it for that year was at an end." *

Even though the Wrights had intended to keep on flying that day until the wind changed their plans, they were elated with the results of the four flights. After they had sent a message to their father describing the flights, the operator at Norfolk—where the message had been first transmitted—asked for permission to give the information to a reporter friend who wrote for the Norfolk *Virginian-Pilot*. The Wrights conferred for a minute and then Wilbur said to the Kitty Hawk operator who had relayed the message, "Tell him no. We want the first news to come from our hometown, not Norfolk."

Although the Kitty Hawk operator, Joseph Dosher, complied, the eager reporter in Norfolk did not honor Wilbur's request. He wrote a story which, according to Orville, "was ninety-nine per cent wrong." This inaccurate report, however, was the first newspaper account of the Wrights' significant technological achievement. A few other newspapers also printed articles, but all were distorted in some way and the Wrights were furious. To correct the inaccuracies, they agreed to give the Associated Press their account, which was printed on January 6, 1904. The report closed with the following statement:

"From the beginning we have employed entirely new

* From "How We Made the First Flight" by Orville Wright, *Flying*, Vol. II, No. 11 (December, 1913), p. 10.

principles of control, and as all the experiments have been conducted at our own expense, without assistance from any individual or institution, we do not feel ready at present to give out any pictures or detailed description of the machine."

This statement showed a new attitude of the Wright brothers. They now viewed their achievement as a potential business enterprise. If they could make the flying machine practical and safe, they could give up the bicycle business and devote full time to manufacturing "aeroplanes."

The reticence of the brothers to describe their machine or release the pictures they had taken at Kitty Hawk caused many to doubt that they had flown at all. Octave Chanute took offense at the Wrights' statement, and the press became divided. The affair became more complicated when Augustus M. Herring, a friend of Chanute's, suggested that the Wrights had copied the construction of his own flying machine. Perhaps, he suggested, he and the Wrights should form a company, each man to have an equal interest so that he would not have to sue.

The Wrights ignored this threat and withdrew from the controversy. They had to protect their invention until they had a clear patent, not only in the United States but in Great Britain, France, Germany, Belgium, and Austria as well. In the meantime, they studied the results of their successful 1903 flights and made ready to give demonstration flights in the summer of 1904, to prove to one and all that they had indeed built a machine unlike any others, that it could be controlled in flight, and that it was dependable and safe.

However, there were unhappy days ahead for Wilbur and Orville Wright. Not only would they have to defend themselves in the courts to protect the rights to their discoveries, but many of their countrymen would seriously doubt that they had truly earned the honor of being the first to fly.

CHAPTER V

A Fight for Recognition

꙳ ꙳ ꙳ ꙳

IF anyone had asked the Wright brothers how much it had cost them from the time of their first glider experiments to the end of their stay in Kitty Hawk in 1903, they would have answered, "less than two thousand dollars." This figure would have included all the parts and supplies for the gliders, the fares to and from Kitty Hawk, the expenses during the experiments, and even the pay of Charley Taylor while he built the engine they had designed. They had neither sought nor received any funds from anyone else, not even from a member of their family. They had made enough from the bicycle business to finance themselves up to this point, and they had managed to save enough to permit them to continue their flying tests while Taylor ran the shop.

In January, 1904, the brothers began to build a new plane. It was similar in design to the 1903 model, but was stronger and about eighty pounds heavier. They designed and started to build three new engines—two of them similar to the original four-cylinder model, and one an eight-cylinder engine.

When the plane was near completion, the Wrights decided to start work on two more of exactly the same design so that all parts would be interchangeable. In case of accident, they reasoned, all they would have to do would be to "cannibalize" one of the other frames for the needed parts. By May, 1904, they decided that they were ready to fly again. They planned to use a pasture next to an interurban railway at Simms Station, eight miles east of Dayton. Known as Huffman Prairie, it is now the site of Wright-Patterson Air Force Base.

Although the Wrights had decided to continue their work in secret, they invited members of the Dayton press to Huffman Prairie on May 26. To this day historians cannot explain why the Wrights did this when they had not yet flown their new model with its new engine. They had asked the press "only . . . that no pictures be taken, and the reports be unsensational."

The brothers soon wished that they had never bothered to invite anyone to witness their first flight in 1904. The engine did not work properly; the wind was calm and the plane could not get an inch off the ground. The Wrights had failed miserably before the eyes of about fifty people.

But they tried again the next day. Although the machine finally did get off the ground, it glided only about sixty feet and slid to an ignominious stop in a cloud of dust. Fortunately, the few reporters who were present the second day did not sensationalize the failure but gave credit to the inventors for trying. However, there were overtones of disbelief in the words of one account written the day before, which stated that the Wright brothers ". . . had another trial near this city today, which the brothers say was successful. Great secrecy was maintained about the test, and but few witnessed it." *

The tone of the press stories, although kind in their reporting of the failures, was general disbelief that the brothers had really accomplished anything spectacular. The Wrights had exposed themselves to the public, and their apparent sincerity prevented them from being publicly ridiculed. The only good result was that they were able to experiment with their plane and practice flying for the rest of the year without arousing further curiosity.

The selection of Huffman Prairie presented technical problems which caused the experimenters much difficulty. The winds were so light and variable that they had to lay a monorail 240 feet into the wind instead of the 60 feet they had used at Kitty Hawk. After a while they discovered that they could get by with a 160-foot monorail, provided the wind was at least eleven miles an hour.

The variance of the wind speed caused a great deal of difficulty, and on one occasion Orville had a narrow escape from serious injury. He slid down the monorail to take advantage of a sudden gust of wind only to have it drop off suddenly as he reached critical flying speed. The plane nosed up briefly and then dove sharply to the ground. Orville was thrown forward as the plane nosed upward. The forward upper-wing spar slammed

* *The New York Times,* May 26, 1904.

48

toward his back but broke just before it made contact. Although they studied this structural failure for a long time, they never were able to figure out what made the spar break a split second before it would have caused serious injury to the pilot.

There was no doubt now that the main problem to be solved was a better launching method to make up for the weak winds. After concentrating on it and debating several possible solutions, they designed a form of catapult consisting of a sort of tripod fitted out with pulleys. A 1,600-pound weight would be hoisted to the top of the tripod and attached by a rope to the end of the plane. When ready to launch, the weight would be tripped. The 350-pound pull thus developed would propel the craft down the track and into the air where the engine and propellers could take hold.

The catapult was first tried on September 7, 1904, and its success was immediate. Longer flights were now made, and in a completely calm wind. However, a new problem developed. Most of the flights had been in a straight line. As the flights got longer, the pilot had to make turns to stay inside the boundaries of the field, which was lined with tall trees. It was discovered all too soon that they had to improve the wing-warping controls to make successful turns. Both men crashed several times, but on September 20, Orville made the first complete 360-degree circle—a significant aviation first. The distance covered on this flight was 4,800 feet.

By the end of their experiments in December, 1904, they had flown a total of 45 minutes and had made over one hundred flights. On November 9, one of them had circled the field four times for a distance of over 3 miles and had stayed aloft 5 minutes and 4 seconds. In one flight they had added a weight of 70 pounds in addition to the pilot. There was no doubt in their minds about what they had done. However, they now wondered what they should do to protect their interests.

The brothers' business knowledge had been proven by the fact that they had applied for a United States patent for their machine in March, 1903—nine months before they actually flew. Other patent applications were submitted to foreign governments soon after, and in March, 1904, France and Great Britain granted them. Germany and the other nations were not yet willing to do so. Ironically, United States patent officials returned the Wrights' application in 1904 and asked them to reword and resubmit it. They did so, but it was not until 1906 that the Wrights received their first American patent.

In the meantime, the brothers continued to work on their plane in relative quiet and seclusion. As their patent applications were being processed, they became the center of scientific interest both at home and abroad. Working through Octave Chanute, who kept them abreast of aeronautical developments, they found that many men were trying to duplicate their experiments. But there were many scientists and writers who still seriously doubted that the Wrights had actually flown at all. Although it rankled the brothers, they followed their course of not seeking publicity and proving their claims until their patents had been assured.

The Wrights decided between them that the year 1905 would be devoted to more flying practice and experimentation with the control system. They agreed that there were too many instances during the 1904 tests when the plane had behaved erratically. Too many flights had ended in crashes and damage to the plane. The close call that Orville had suffered made them realize that death was a very real possibility. As a result, they concentrated on improving rather than changing their basic design.

Since there was the possibility that someone might steal their hard-won knowledge, the Wrights began the 1905 testing session in secrecy—as well as they could with a trolley car running right by the testing field on a regular schedule. They timed their tests to avoid having the passengers see them in flight, and were fairly successful.

The 1905 airframe and the engine were almost the same as those used the year before, except that the wings had been restressed and the camber had been changed. Slight changes were also made in the propellers and the front and rear rudders for greater stability and control. Still flying from the horizontal position, the Wrights also made some improvements for the pilot's comfort.

The summer months came and went and the flights became longer and more successful. During the last two weeks of September, with exceptionally good weather prevailing, they made more flights than they had in all their previous years. On September 26, one of them flew a distance of over ten miles in a circling course for the first time.

Encouraged by each success, the brothers flew fifteen miles on October 3, and over twenty miles the next day, still within the confines of Huffman Prairie. On October 5, Wilbur made a flight covering over twenty-four miles, and stayed aloft for 38 minutes and 4 seconds.

Looking back over their experimental records for the 1903–5 time period, they calculated that they had improved the weight-lifting ability of their machine from 745 to 925 pounds. Speed had increased from 30 to 38 miles per hour, and they had stayed aloft more than a half hour and covered almost 25 miles in distance. Total flight distance they had achieved now amounted to more than 160 miles.

It was inevitable that word would soon spread that "those crazy Wright brothers" really were flying their machine. In spite of the Wrights' attempts to prevent the flights from being observed, many citizens in the Dayton area saw them circling the field and heard their engine put-putting during the daylight hours in good weather. The word spread slowly but surely. Their mail from the curious increased, and newspaper and magazine articles rumored that the Wrights had made great scientific strides in the science of flight.

The Wrights' reaction was typical of anyone who has a patent pending. They were afraid their machine would be copied, and they retreated into silence while they carried on negotiations to obtain their patents and find buyers for their machines. The brothers made a significant decision that guided their planning. They would sell only to a government, not to an individual. They would form a stock company only if they viewed it necessary to obtain capital. In the meantime, they would resist publicizing what they had accomplished and would attend to the business of negotiations.

How much they feared having their invention stolen

cannot be overemphasized. After the last flight of 1905, they dismantled their plane, hauled it back to their shop in Dayton, and did not fly again for the next two and a half years. But they were constantly torn between defending their claims of accomplishments and hiding the machine that had made them. In a letter to the editor of the *Scientific American* they had described their 1905 flights, hoping that the editor would help them refute the disbelief of the scientific world.

Instead, the editor doubted the Wrights' claims and published a cynical article in the January 13, 1906, issue entitled, "The Wright Aeroplane and Its Fabled Performances." The editor wrote: "If such sensational and tremendously important experiments are being conducted in a not very remote part of the country, on a subject in which almost everybody feels the most profound interest, is it possible to believe that the enterprising American reporter, who, it is well known, comes down the chimney when the door is locked in his face —even if he has to scale a fifteen-story skyscraper to do so—would not have ascertained all about them and published their broadcast long ago?"

Proof was demanded by the Aero Club of America, and the Wrights promptly furnished a list of citizens of the Dayton area who had seen some of the flights. The editor of the *Scientific American* also demanded names. Letters were written to each person whom the Wrights had named and all confirmed what they had seen, much to the surprise of the doubters. In an editorial on December 15, 1906, the *Scientific American* observed that "in all the history of invention, there is probably no parallel to the unostentatious manner in which the

THE WRIGHT BROTHERS

Wright brothers of Dayton, Ohio, ushered into the
world their epoch-making invention of the first successful aeroplane flying machine."

The magazine editor and others were not the only
ones who had doubted that the Wrights had actually
flown. The brothers had written to R. M. Nevin, the
congressman from their district, and had told him of
their successes that had "ended in the production of a
flying machine of a type fitted for use." They asked if
Nevin could "find it convenient to ascertain whether
this is a subject of interest to our own government."
Nevin sent the letter to the Board of Ordnance and
Fortifications in the War Department.

Weeks went by, and finally the Wrights received a
reply from Major General G. L. Gillespie, president of
the board, stating that "the Board has found it necessary to decline to make allotments for the experimental
development of devices for mechanical flight, and has
determined that, before suggestions with that object in
view will be considered, the device must have been
brought to the stage of practical operation without expense to the United States."

The Wrights were furious at such a reply. They had
not asked for any funds from the government, and
their "device" had already flown. If the United States
was not interested, they then felt free to carry on negotiations with foreign governments. However, they tried
once more. They wrote to the Secretary of War offering
to furnish "practical flying machines suitable for scouting purposes." They did not want to take their invention abroad, they said, "unless we find it necessary to do
so, and therefore write again, renewing the offer."

Again the brothers were rebuffed by an answer that said the board could not consider a flying machine such as the Wrights offered unless the board could receive "cost estimates and delivery dates and such drawings and descriptions thereof as are necessary to enable its construction to be understood and a definite conclusion as to its practicality to be arrived at."

The Wrights promptly responded that they could not make estimates, propose a delivery date, or furnish drawings, until they knew what government specifications they had to meet. The recorder for the board answered that the board "does not care to formulate any requirements for the performance of a flying machine or take any further action on the subject until a machine is produced which by actual operation is shown to be able to produce horizontal flight and to carry an operator."

Although the United States government was not interested, many individuals were. Numerous queries were received, most of them from French interests. The best offer was from Arnold Fordyce and a French syndicate who agreed to pay one million francs for the option to purchase a flying machine capable of a fifty-kilometer flight. This offer fell through when the money could not be raised to support it. The Wrights wrote letters to appropriate officials of other governments, including Russia, Italy, and Japan.

One of the major difficulties in negotiations was that the Wrights would not furnish drawings or photographs, nor would they fly their plane for prospective buyers to prove to them that their claims were valid. In May, 1906, however, United States Patent No. 821,393 was granted, and their greatest reason for secrecy vanished. At Chanute's begging, and because so many men were getting close to constructing successful machines, the Wrights began to be concerned. Santos-Dumont, a celebrated airship pilot, was on the verge of getting a heavier-than-air machine into the air in France in August, 1906. A Dane, U. C. H. Ellehammer, rose briefly off the ground for a few seconds in September. Santos-Dumont became airborne for less than a minute in October and made several more successful flights in November. Ironically, this flamboyant Brazilian was widely acclaimed for his feats of airmanship even though his longest flight had been only 722 feet and he had not yet made a 360-degree turn. In contrast to the Wrights, Santos-Dumont did not attempt to conceal his control mechanism and was willing to show the world what he and his machine could do. In spite of the criticism against them in the press and the apparent acclamation that Santos-Dumont was getting, the Wrights still would not let their secrets loose. By the beginning of 1907, their names were fading from public mention in favor of the Brazilian.

The continual negotiations with half a dozen governments and a number of influential individuals at home and abroad enlarged the circle of contacts for the Wrights. Chanute's never-ending interest and advice enabled them to meet other aeronauts and such men as Glenn H. Curtiss, an engine manufacturer, and Alexander Graham Bell, inventor of the telephone. Although not one of these men had seen the Wrights fly, they respected the evidence that the brothers furnished and the testimony of Chanute who had seen them in the air. But the year was to be a turning point for the Wrights. On August 1, 1907, the War Department established an Aeronautical Division within the Signal Corps for the "study of the flying machine and the possibility of adapting it to military purpose."

CHAPTER VI

Contracts and Records

THE simple, fragile machine that the Wright brothers took aloft on a raw December day in 1903 foreshadowed developments of great importance for military aeronautics and the science of war. The achievement of controlled flight made it possible to produce an aerial weapon that could take the offensive instead of being used merely for reconnaissance. However, even the first heavier-than-air craft were considered only for their possible usefulness as scouting planes rather than as planes that could drop bombs on an enemy or shoot down enemy planes in aerial combat. It was inevitable that once the Wrights proved that man could leave the ground under power, maneuver, fly for extended periods of time, and return safely, new and deadlier uses would be discovered for wartime needs.

The United States War Department had been interested in heavier-than-air flying machines since 1898. Dr. Samuel P. Langley, a distinguished scientist and secretary of the Smithsonian Institution, had flown powered models as early as 1896. One of them flew three-quarters of a mile until the naphtha powering its steam engine ran out. On the basis of this performance, the U.S. government granted him fifty thousand dollars to build a man-carrying airplane. Its two tests—the second on December 8, 1903, nine days before the Wrights' successes at Kitty Hawk—were highly publicized. Although the tests were unsuccessful, Langley was convinced that the launching mechanisms were at fault rather than his "aerodrome." But because of his failures, he could not raise the funds to build another machine.

The Army's lack of enthusiasm for the claims of the Wright brothers can be understood when it is realized that Army leaders were severely criticized for spending taxpayers' money on the Langley machine. But by the summer of 1907 things had changed. The Aero Club of America contacted President Theodore Roosevelt on behalf of the Wright brothers, but the request to allow the Wrights to demonstrate their machine was denied. After the Aeronautical Division of the Signal Corps was formed on August 1, 1907, the Wrights received an invitation to meet with the Board of Ordnance and Fortifications. At this meeting, the Wrights told the board what they thought their machine could do, and offered it to the Army for twenty-five thousand dollars.

It took several weeks for the board, under the leadership of Major George O. Squier, to announce Specification No. 486 to the public for a "flying machine." Sealed bids were to be turned in to the Signal Corps no later than noon on February 1, 1908.

Based on what the Wrights had said their machine could do, the board specified that the flying machine the Army would buy had to fly 40 miles an hour, be able to carry two people whose combined weight would not exceed 350 pounds, and be able to stay in the air for one hour. In addition, it had to "be capable of landing and taking off, without undue delay, and also be capable of dismounting and loading on an Army wagon to be transported." As an afterthought, the board specified that the machine had to be so constructed that it would "permit an intelligent man to become proficient in its use within a reasonable length of time." Two pilots had to be trained by the designer whose plane won the competition.

As soon as the specifications were announced, newspapers across the country criticized this new effort to spend taxpayers' money foolishly. The New York *Globe* editorialized as follows:

"One might be inclined to assume from the following announcement, 'the United States Army is asking for bids for a military airship,' that the era of practical human flight had arrived, or at least that the government had seriously taken up the problem of developing this means of travel.

"A very brief examination of the conditions imposed and the reward offered for successful bidders suffices, however, to prove this assumption a delusion.

"A machine such as described in the Signal Corps specifications would record the solution of all the difficulties in the way of the heavier-than-air airship, and, in fact, finally give mankind almost as complete control of the air as it now has of the land and the water.

"It would be worth to the world almost any number of millions of dollars, would certainly revolutionize warfare and possibly the transportation of passengers; would open to easy access regions hitherto inaccessible except to the most daring pioneers and would, in short, be probably the most epoch-making invention in the history of civilization.

"Nothing in any way approaching such a machine has ever been constructed—the Wright brothers' claim still awaits public confirmation—and the man who has achieved such a success would have, or at least should have, no need of competing in a contest where the successful bidder might be given his trial because his offer was a few hundred or thousand dollars lower than that of someone else.

"If there is any possibility that such an airship is within measurable distance of perfection, any government could well afford to provide its inventor with unlimited resources and promise him a prize, in case of success, running into the millions."

A highly respected aviation magazine of the day added to the criticism of the press. Its editor wrote that "There is not a known flying machine in the world which could fulfill these specifications at the present moment." He added: "Perhaps the Signal Corps has been too much influenced by the 'hot air' of theorizers, in which aeronautics unfortunately abounds, who have fathomed the entire problem without ever accomplishing anything; talk is their stock in trade and models of machines are beneath them because they are beyond their impractical nature. Why is not the experience with Professor Langley a good guide? We doubt very much if the government receives any bids at all possible to be accepted."

But the Army did receive bids. Forty-one of them, in fact, ranging from $1,000 to $10,000,000. Only three of them were considered valid, however, including the bid of $25,000 by the Wright brothers. At the deadline date only the Wrights were left, and the contract for the delivery of one "aeroplane" was signed with them.

The contract contained an interesting stipulation which gave an added incentive to the men from Dayton. The government would increase the award by 10 per cent for each mile an hour over the 40-mph speed. Therefore, if they could average 45 miles per hour instead of 40, the bonus to be added to the $25,000 price would be an additional $12,500. On the other hand, 10 per cent would be deducted from the price for each mile per hour under the 40-mile speed of the specifications, with a minimum set at 35 miles per hour.

The Wrights readily agreed to this stipulation and immediately set to work on a plane that would satisfy the Army. At the same time, they had received word that the French government might be close to offering a contract. As a result, the brothers planned to build a total of six planes by the summer of 1908.

Now the Wrights were running a race against time. On January 13, 1908, Henri Farman won the Deutsch-Archdeacon prize of fifty thousand francs, or ten thousand dollars, for flying over one kilometer in a closed circle, and received worldwide acclaim. Then Leon Delogrange, a sculptor, made the first flight in history with a passenger, who happened to be Henri Farman.

In the United States the first public flying demonstration was made on March 9, 1908, when the *Red Wing*, a plane designed for the Aerial Experiment Association of Hammondsport, New York, took to the air briefly from a frozen lake before crashing. The *White Wing* flew in May and was a little more successful, but none of these flights measured up to what the Wrights had done three years before.

The Wrights were unperturbed by speculation that their records would soon be surpassed. They returned to Kitty Hawk in May, 1908, repaired their old buildings, and practiced flying in the same plane they had packed away in 1905, altering it to meet the government specifications. As they described it in a magazine article, "The operator assumed a sitting position, instead of lying prone, as in 1905, and a seat was added for a passenger. A larger motor was installed, and the radiators and gasoline reservoirs of larger capacity replaced those previously used."

Although they made no attempts at distance, speed, altitude, or endurance records, they did take up a passenger (Charles W. Furnas) on May 14, 1908, for the first time. Later that day, Wilbur damaged the plane on landing and concluded their experiments. However, they were satisfied with what they had done because "the machine showed a speed of nearly 41 miles per hour with two men on board, and a little over 44 miles with one man. The control was very satisfactory in winds of 15 to 20 miles an hour, and there was no distinguishable difference in control when traveling with, against, or across the wind." *

When the brothers returned to Dayton, they decided that Wilbur would go to France to demonstrate their

* Wright, "Our Aeroplane Tests at Kitty Hawk," *Scientific American* (June 13, 1908), p. 423.

plane while Orville would stay in the United States to prepare for the War Department tests at Fort Myer, Virginia. While they had been practicing at Kitty Hawk, their European contacts had negotiated a contract with a French commercial syndicate. A contract had been signed requiring the Wright plane to make two flights of 50 kilometers (31 miles) each, with a passenger aboard. The contract also stipulated that the Wrights were to teach three men to fly. All this had to be accomplished within one week. If they could carry out these terms, the Wrights were to receive 500,000 francs ($100,000). In addition, they would sell four machines to the syndicate for 80,000 francs ($16,000).

Wilbur arrived in France in July and calmly set about preparing to fly. He chose a racetrack near Le Mans as his flying field. To his chagrin, he found both the British press and the French press hostile to him, because few Europeans really believed that the Wrights had flown as they had claimed. A sensitive man, Wilbur refused to grant interviews and proceeded at a leisurely pace to assemble his plane. On August 8, 1908, he flew for the first time, and although the flight lasted only 1 minute and 45 seconds, he showed such control of his plane that the French skeptics were amazed. He flew every day for the next week and increased his time in the air to the point where he circled the field seven times.

The Europeans now no longer doubted. None of their own pilots, whom they had acclaimed so highly, had ever come close to such a performance. This quiet man, who avoided crowds, disliked the press, and lived so simply, was completely different from the showmen who had bragged and then failed to achieve even the simplest of the Wright maneuvers.

The field at Le Mans soon proved too small, and Wilbur moved to another near Auvours where large crowds quickly assembled every day. The French press treated the flights as the biggest news of the century. One newspaper, *Le Figaro,* commented: "It was not merely a success; a conclusive trial and a decisive victory for aviation, the news of which will revolutionize scientific circles throughout the world!"

Wilbur continued his flying whenever the weather was favorable. He took up Ernest Zens—his first passenger there—on September 16. A few days later, he flew 40 miles in 1 hour, 31 minutes, without a passenger. Then, on October 6, he flew with a passenger for 1 hour, 4½ minutes, the longest flight yet made by two persons. The next day he took Mrs. Hart O. Berg up for a short flight, giving her the honor of being the first woman passenger in an airplane.

Each passing day seemed to produce more firsts and new world records. Since he was required to train three pilots, Wilbur began his teaching on October 28. The three students were Count Charles de Lambert, Paul Tissandier, and Captain Lucas de Girardville.

The Aero Club of France offered several prizes during Wilbur's stay at Auvours. First was a prize for attaining an altitude of 25 meters which, it was hoped, one of several French planes would win. Then another prize was offered for the first to achieve 30 meters. Wilbur won both by climbing to 90 meters.

By December, Wilbur was still going strong. He performed the first "dead stick" landing by shutting off the engine at an altitude of 200 feet and gliding to a safe landing. On December 18, he stayed aloft for 1 hour and 55 minutes, and on the same day won another prize by reaching an altitude of 110 meters, a new world's record.

On the last day of 1908, Wilbur set a final record at Auvours. He made an endurance flight of 2 hours, 20 minutes, and won another prize. In all, he had won 24,500 francs ($4,900) and set a number of world records.

Wilbur left Auvours in January, 1909, and began operations in Paris, where the weather was warmer. Here he would be joined by Orville and their sister Katharine. While Wilbur had enjoyed great triumphs abroad, Orville had experienced great tragedy at home.

CHAPTER VII

The Beginnings of the Air Force

WHILE Wilbur was in Europe, Orville readied himself and his plane for flight tests at Fort Myer, Virginia, near the nation's capital. It had been decided, after the formation of the Aeronautical Division of the Signal Corps, that the Army should test both the dirigible and the airplane to see what potential each had for military use. A contract had been signed with Thomas Scott Baldwin for an airship to be powered by an engine designed and built by Glenn Curtiss. The airship would be tested just before tests would be run on the Wright Flyer.

Baldwin and his airship arrived on July 23, and by August 12 had passed all the tests. Baldwin acted as pilot and Curtiss acted as engineer. As part of the contract, three military men—Lieutenants Benjamin D. Foulois, Frank P. Lahm, and Thomas E. Selfridge—were taught to fly it. Baldwin, happy in the knowledge that his airship had fulfilled its contract, packed up his gear and moved out.

Orville arrived at Fort Myer on August 20 and was assigned an old shed on the parade ground located beside Arlington Cemetery. Assisted by Charley Taylor and Charley Furnas, he assembled the Flyer and made his first flight on September 3, 1908.

Actually, the youngest of the Wright brothers was apprehensive about the tests because the parade ground was only about seven hundred by one thousand feet, and was surrounded by tall trees and barracks buildings. Neither of the brothers had ever made a flight within so confined a space.

There were only about five hundred people present on that day, in spite of the coverage given in the papers. After an extremely long period of preflight inspection, during which the crowd became very impatient, Orville finally climbed into the seat and gave the command to start the engine. Taylor and Furnas turned the propellers and stood at each wing tip as Orville warmed up the engine. When ready, he nodded to his helpers and triggered the starting device. The Flyer leaped forward as the weight on the starting tower crashed to the ground. The flimsy machine, with engine wide open, slipped down the launching track and into the air. A cheer went up from the spectators, most of whom had been skeptical that this frail man in the high collar could do what had been claimed.

Orville made a turn and a half around the parade ground and landed after 1 minute and 11 seconds of flight. However, the landing was a hard one and he nearly skidded into a tent. There was a loud crack and one of the skids broke as the craft came to a dusty halt.

Orville repaired the runner with a piece of lumber

from a local yard and took to the air again. By September 9 he had established several world endurance records. On that morning he circled the parade ground fifty-seven times in as many minutes and later that day made a flight of 1 hour and 2 minutes. On the same day, he invited Lieutenant Frank P. Lahm along as passenger and circled the field six times in 6½ minutes. Thus, Lahm had the honor of being the first American military man to be an airplane passenger.

Orville continued to break his own endurance records over the next two days. He made two figure eights around the field on September 11, and stayed aloft 1 hour and 10 minutes. Then on September 12 he took Major George O. Squier along as a passenger and set a new two-man flight record of just over 9 minutes. To top off this performance, he flew for 1 hour and 15 minutes, during which time he reached a height of 300 feet to establish still another record for a one-man flight.

After that it was five days before Orville could get the Flyer into the air again. Excessive winds and maintenance problems prevented him from continuing, but the news of his successes had spread far and wide. His record-shattering flights surprised a skeptical public and shoved the other news off the front pages. The unbelievable feats performed by Orville were being repeated by Wilbur in Europe, and the thought thrilled the world. These two quiet men, by their amazing performances an ocean apart, had suddenly raised the possibility of flight in heavier-than-air machines from the status of a foolish dream into the world of fact. The more reporters researched the story, the more fascinating the success of the Wrights became. Working alone, without the backing of money interests and the barking of publicity agents, these modest, confident, careful brothers had become the first truly successful airplane pilots in history.

The extensive newspaper coverage of the Wrights' story caused a huge crowd to gather at Fort Myer on September 17 to watch Orville's Flyer. Thomas Selfridge, the young West Point graduate, had asked to be a passenger because of his interest in the Glenn Curtiss experiments. Since he did not weigh too much, and the Army had no objections, Orville had agreed.

It was exactly 5:14 P.M. when the Flyer started down the launching track. The plane seemed to take longer than ever to get off the ground, and once off it did not seem as though it would climb more than a foot above the grass. Slowly the machine clawed for altitude, and at the far end of the field started a gradual turn back toward the starting point. To those on the ground, the Flyer seemed to operate a little sluggishly, but as it made one complete turn, followed by two more, Orville gradually coaxed more altitude out of it, and the crowd relaxed.

At the beginning of the fourth circle and at an altitude of about 125 feet, Orville heard behind him a slapping noise of metal against metal. It sounded like the chain drive running from the engine to one of the propellers. He turned quickly, and although he saw nothing, his experience told him to land immediately. The sound got louder and he knew that something was drastically wrong. "Hang on," he told Selfridge, "we're going down!"

Hardly had he shouted the words than two big thumps proved that something was indeed wrong. Orville quickly shut off the motor, just as the plane began to swerve from side to side and shake violently. The machine rapidly lost flying speed, and Orville saw that they were headed toward a drainage ditch. With the small reserve of speed still left, he turned the craft toward the parade grounds for a crosswind landing. The frail plane, riding on the thin edge of a stall, nosed down sharply. To regain flying speed, Orville pushed the elevators forward as far as they would go. The plane recovered momentarily from its downward plunge as it crossed the field boundary. At about twenty-five feet above the ground, however, the Flyer stalled and plunged earthward. There was nothing that Orville could do. The fragile machine with its two fragile humans struck the ground in a grinding, nerve-shattering crash.

In a split second, what had been a graceful man-made bird had become a crumpled mass of muslin, wood, and metal. Women in the crowd screamed. Soldiers rushed forward and immediately began to push the wreckage aside to get at Wright and Selfridge. First to be extricated was Orville, who was immediately rushed to the post hospital. He had sustained a broken thigh, several broken ribs, and severe cuts and bruises.

It took longer to get Selfridge out because he was pinned beneath the engine. When the soldiers reached him, his only words were "Please get this thing off my back."

By the time Selfridge was pulled out of the wreckage,

he was unconscious, having suffered a fractured skull and severe face cuts. He was immediately rushed to Walter Reed Army Hospital in Washington where the finest Army surgeons operated on him. But their best efforts were not good enough. Tom Selfridge died three hours later—the first man in the history of heavier-than-air flight to give his life for aviation.

* * * * * *

The day after the tragic accident, the mechanics, Taylor and Furnas, went to the post hospital to see Orville. Although in pain from his own injuries, his greatest concern was for Selfridge.

"How did it happen, Charley?" he asked Taylor.

"I'm not sure, Mr. Wright, but let me show you what I found."

Taylor and Furnas went out in the hallway and brought back a broken propeller and some metal parts. Orville stared at the objects.

"It was the propeller, wasn't it, Charley?"

Taylor nodded. Two new propellers, eight inches longer than any used before, had been installed just before the flight. One of them developed a long crack in flight, which caused it to flatten out and vibrate unevenly. At the high speed the blade was turning, the vibration rapidly got worse, causing the propeller housing and the chain drive to shake and pound against the frame. One of the guy wires running back to the tail assembly tore loose, causing the tail to rise and the nose to lower. This was the reason why Orville had found the elevator controls unresponsive when he had tried to glide to a safe landing.

Knowing the cause of the accident did not lessen the burden of the tragedy. Orville brooded over Selfridge's death and was on the verge of giving up flying when Octave Chanute arrived, followed by Katharine Wright. Between them, they convinced Orville that he and Wilbur, by their achievements at home and abroad, had proven beyond any doubt that the flying machine was a reality. Lying flat on his back, the younger Wright began thinking and planning again for the future. If the Army would let him, he told Chanute, he would continue the tests the next summer.

Orville did not need to worry about the Army giving him another chance. The day after the accident, Major George O. Squire gave a prepared statement to the press. He said that the accident was "simply a temporary setback."

"Of course, we deplore the accident," the statement said, "but no one who saw the flights of the last four days at Fort Myer could doubt for an instant that the problem of aerial navigation was solved.

"If Mr. Wright should never again enter an aeroplane, his work last week at Fort Myer will have secured him a lasting place in history as the man who showed the world that mechanical flight was an assured success. No one seems to realize at this close range what a revolution the flights portend. The problem is solved and it remains only to work out the details."

In Europe, Wilbur was shocked and saddened by the accident and immediately wrote to Katharine. "I cannot help thinking over and over again," he said, "if I had been there, it would not have happened. . . . I do not mean that Orville was incompetent to do

the work itself, but I realized that he would be surrounded by thousands of people who with the most
friendly intentions in the world would consume his
time, exhaust his strength, and keep him from having
proper rest. . . . When we take up the American
demonstration again, we will both be there."

The elder Wright brother added: "Tell 'Bubbo'
that his flights have revolutionized the world's beliefs
regarding the practicability of flight. Even such con-
servative papers as the London *Times* devote leading
editorials to his work and accept human flight as a
thing to be regarded as a normal feature of the world's
future lift."

Wilbur worried deeply about his brother, but continued his record-breaking flights in France. At the end
of September, when Orville's recovery was assured,
the seventy-six-year-old Chanute wrote a reassuring
letter to Wilbur saying that Orville "was pronounced
quite out of danger and his broken leg had so far
knitted that the surgeon told me that it would not be
more than one-eighth shorter than the other. His
temperature, which had been $101\frac{4}{5}$ part of the time,
had become normal, and although he was still weak
(having been fed with liquid food) , he had recovered
his pluck and mental poise; the old genial smile had
come back."

In the weeks following, Wilbur wrote encouraging
letters to his brother telling him in great detail of his
flights and the prizes that he had won. He delighted
especially in telling of the change of heart of many of
the European writers who had come to doubt and who
had stayed to praise his accomplishments. In one letter

he said, "Every day there is a crowd of people here not only from the neighborhood, but also from almost every country of Europe. Queen Margherita of Italy was in the crowd yesterday. Princes and millionaires are as thick as flies."

As soon as he could use crutches, Orville returned to Dayton to continue his recuperation. He received a letter every two or three days from Wilbur telling of the honors, medals, and accolades "they" were receiving. While many clubs and organizations there wanted to honor Wilbur alone, the elder brother refused singular recognition. He wrote to his father on one occasion that "the government had decided to confer upon me the 'Legion of Honor' but on learning of it privately, I sent word that it would be impossible for me to accept an honor which Orville could not equally share." He added that he had been offered the honorary presidency of a new English aeroplane society, "but I declined it as I have declined all formal honors in which Orville was not associated."

Orville did not write to his brother until the middle of November, 1908. In this first letter he described the accident in great detail and then added in a chiding aside, "I do not like the idea of your attempting a channel flight when I am not present. I haven't much faith in your motor running. You seem to have more trouble with the engine than I do." What had provoked this kidding was a mention in one of Wilbur's letters that the London *Daily Mail* was offering $12,500 for a cross-channel flight, plus half the net receipts of an exhibition of the machine in London.

There is no doubt that Wilbur's successes in Europe

hastened Orville's recovery. Wilbur asked his brother and sister to join him in France as soon as possible. Shortly after the beginning of 1909, Orville and Katharine landed at Le Havre and joined Wilbur near the Spanish border, where the elder brother was training the three French pilots. When the training was completed, the Wrights went to Rome where Wilbur demonstrated their machine to an Italian company, or "aviation club," which had been formed to buy a plane. Wilbur trained two pilots there, and then the Wrights received an offer from some wealthy Germans to form a German Wright company. The brothers signed a preliminary contract which provided that they would receive cash, stock in the company, and a ten per cent royalty on all planes sold.

The Wright trio went to Paris and London from Rome, and received more honors and awards. Exhausted but exhilarated, they returned to the United States in May. Five weeks later, the two men who had been ignored when they were making history at Huffman's Prairie were given a two-day celebration with cannon salutes, a parade, a ten-minute factory-whistle salute, and night fireworks. They received three medals at a special ceremony—one from the city of Dayton, another from the state of Ohio, and, most significantly, one from the Congress of the United States, conferred by General James Allen, chief signal officer of the United States Army.

When the homecoming celebrations were over, the Wright brothers knew what they would have to do next. They had to return to Fort Myer with a new machine and complete the Army tests. They arrived there in June, 1909, and the first flight was made on June 28.

There was an unspoken agreement between them that Orville would be the pilot for the tests, even though he had not flown since the accident the year before. But this time Wilbur was there to double-check the assembly and preparation of the plane for flight. They were determined that no mechanical failure would prevent them from carrying out the rest of the conditions of the Army specifications.

A number of preliminary flights, all by Orville, were made between June 28 and July 27. On the latter date, Orville announced that he was ready to resume the tests, and he chose to comply with the specification calling for a "trial endurance flight of at least one hour" and another requiring that the plane "be designed to carry two persons having a combined weight of about 350 pounds." He chose the tall, slim Frank Lahm as passenger, and complied with both specifications by staying aloft with Lahm for 1 hour, 12 minutes, and 40 seconds —a world's record for a two-man flight.

On July 30, Orville told the Aeronautical Board that he was ready to attempt the crucial part of the specifications—the cross-country and speed tests. Orville chose Benjamin Foulois as his passenger and official observer. Weighing only about 135 pounds, the wiry Foulois had helped the Wrights to assemble their plane, and they took an immediate liking to him. A former enlisted man who had won a commission while on duty in the Philippines, Foulois was assigned duties as a navigator for the ten-mile cross-country flight.

The test course was laid out from the Fort Myer

parade ground to Shuter's Hill in Alexandria, Virginia, the site of the famous Masonic Temple, which was then being constructed. They were to circle a captive balloon sent aloft as a marker and return to Fort Myer.

Foulois, later a major general and chief of the Air Corps, recalled that memorable day. He told the author:

"We got off at approximately 6:45 P.M. and fortunately for my peace of mind, I was kept so fully occupied with my jobs as Observer and Navigator on the outbound flight that I had no time to worry about a treetop landing. However, upon reaching the turning point at Shuter's Hill, Orville, presumably for the benefit of the ground observers at that point, came in low and rounded the group of trees, and then squared away on the homebound trip. A fine demonstration of his piloting skill but, as I told him later, a bit too close to the treetops to suit me. On the homebound flight, however, we ran into a downtrend of air which dropped the airplane to about twenty-five feet from the treetops and I began to wonder which clump of trees Orville would pick out for his landing place. The little engine, however, continued to behave and, with the best pilot in the world at the controls, we climbed back to our normal altitude—thence over Arlington Cemetery and in to a perfect landing at Fort Myer, where we were happily greeted by Wilbur Wright, who I later learned had experienced a few unhappy moments when the downtrend dropped us out of sight on the homebound flight. I also learned later that, as the airplane arrived over the edge of Arlington Cemetery adjacent to the

Fort Myer parade ground, some of the spectators, numbering approximately six to eight thousand, had voiced their enthusiasm in connection with our safe return.

"Judging, however, from my personal experience with the normal crowd of spectators which had thronged about the Fort Myer parade ground during all of the prior test flights, I had no doubt that there were also many bloodthirsty individuals present who returned to their homes sorely disappointed because we had failed to land in Arlington Cemetery and thus provide them with a real old-fashioned 'Roman Holiday' with all its bloody trimmings.

"Thus ended my first flight in a heavier-than-air flying machine; a flight which, as I recall, established three records for two-man flight; speed 42.5 miles per hour (average) ; cross-country, 10 miles (round trip) ; and altitude 400 feet (approx.) ."

Thus, the Wright Flyer had met all the requirements of the Army contract. Since the machine had achieved a speed of two miles per hour over the desired forty, the Wrights were awarded thirty thousand dollars. However, a token payment of twenty thousand dollars was made because there still remained one unfulfilled clause in the contract. Two men had to be instructed "in the handling and operation of this flying machine."

Lieutenants Lahm and Foulois were designated as the two officers to be taught to fly, but Foulois was ordered to Europe on temporary duty and was replaced by Lieutenant Frederic E. Humphreys, an officer assigned to the Corps of Engineers. However, the post commander at Fort Myer did not want any more flying from his parade grounds, and he ordered the Wrights to find another field. They then decided that Wilbur should do the instructing while Orville would go to Germany to continue negotiating with the German interests.

Lieutenant Lahm had anticipated the unsympathetic reaction to further Fort Myer tests and had chosen a field at College Park, Maryland, to establish the first flying school. After a few instructional flights, both officers were ready to solo. On October 26, Humphreys and then Lahm soloed—the first men in American uniform to do so. Ironically, Humphreys returned to duty with the Corps of Engineers shortly thereafter and never became a rated military pilot. Lahm was also ordered back to duty with troops.

In the meantime, Lieutenant Foulois returned from Europe and was given instruction by Wilbur, but he did not solo. The Wrights had more than fulfilled their contract by instructing three men instead of two. However, because the first two men were sent back to other duties in the Army, the government now had Airplane No. 1, and no pilots. Foulois was the only man left who had had any instruction, and the Wrights could stay no longer. By the end of November, the entire combat air arm of the United States consisted of one badly damaged airplane (Lahm had ended his last flight in a crash), eight enlisted mechanics, one civilian mechanic, and a pilot who had never flown alone.

This did not bother the peppery Foulois. As he recalled, ". . . I was not entirely unqualified. I had logged fifty-four minutes of passenger time with Wilbur Wright before the final test. He had even allowed me to handle the controls."

What did bother Foulois, though, was that General Allen, the Chief Signal Officer, told him, "Lieutenant, I've decided to send you and your flying machine to Texas where the weather is better."

"Yes, sir. Do you have any special instructions for me?"

"Your orders are simple, Lieutenant. You are to test the airplane for the Army. Just take plenty of spare parts—and teach yourself to fly."

Foulois did as he was told, and for the next two years was a one-man air force. He literally taught himself to fly by correspondence with the Wrights. On the first day that he flew at San Antonio, he accomplished his first takeoff, first solo, first landing, and first crash. He crashed frequently, but, strangely, was never injured. In fact, in all of his next twenty-five years of flying, he suffered only one injury and that was a wire burn that occurred when a stay wire pinned his leg to the ground after a particularly hard landing. However, after each crash or after the plane suffered any damage, Foulois quickly explained what he had done in a letter to the Wrights, and they promptly answered from wherever they were. He would repair "Old No. 1" as best he could and try again.

The indomitable Foulois continued his flying career until he retired as head of the Air Corps, in 1935. During that time, he achieved many aviation firsts, such as the first to use a safety belt, the first to install wheels on an airplane, and the first to send and receive a radio message from a plane. He later became the first United States combat pilot during the Pershing Punitive Expedition to Mexico, and was also head of American flying units in France during World War I. It was through this man and the thousands who followed him that the Wrights realized their personal desires to have their own government adopt and develop their brainchild.

CHAPTER VIII
The End of the Partnership

WITH the test flights at Fort Myer successfully completed, Orville and his sister Katharine left the United States for Germany. The German Wright company had now been formed, and a German pilot had to be trained. Exhibition flights would be made to demonstrate the capabilities of the Wright machine.

Orville's first flights were made at Tempelhof, a huge military parade ground in Berlin, now the major airport in West Berlin. The first flights were so successful that the danger of flying was nothing compared to the danger that German crowds presented as they mobbed Orville after each flight. Since he could not speak German, the crowds pressed forward just to touch him. German soldiers were assigned to form a cordon around him to protect him from being crushed.

Orville set new world's records within a month after his arrival. On September 16, 1909, he established a new altitude record of 172 meters. On the eighteenth, he flew for 1 hour, 35 minutes, with a passenger, Captain Paul Englehardt, to set a new endurance record for two-man flight. On October 2, he took the German Crown Prince Frederick Wilhelm up for a fifteen-minute flight, which made the Prince the first member of a royal family ever to ride in an airplane.

During one of the flights which started late in the afternoon, Orville stayed up longer than he intended. Although it seemed light enough at his altitude, it was darker near the ground than he realized. Many of the spectators, figuring that he might need lights, helpfully turned on their automobile lights. As far as can be determined, this night landing was the first ever made in an airplane.

While Orville was pleasing the crowds in Germany, Wilbur was making sensational flights in the United States. Millions of people watched as he made the first flights over the Statue of Liberty, Governors Island, Grant's Tomb, and up the Hudson River in New York. On October 4, Wilbur flew from the parade ground at Governors Island up the Hudson and back for a distance of twenty-one miles—a new distance record. For this flight, mostly over water, Wilbur had lashed a canoe between the skids of the Flyer, which he hoped would act as a pontoon if he made a forced landing.

Orville returned from Europe in November. He had checked on the growth of the French Wright company and had observed that little progress had been made in the sale of Wright planes to the French government. Nevertheless, the French and the German companies were legally formed. It now remained for the officials to convince the two governments that the rights to manufacture the Wright machine should be bought without more delay.

Oddly, although the Wrights had proven their machine in the United States, no group of American investors came forward to propose the formation of an American Wright company which would produce planes in quantity. It was true that offers had been received from individuals but none of them were substantial enough for the Wrights to take seriously.

It remained for twenty-four-year-old Clinton R. Peterkin to make the financial breakthrough. A former office boy with J. P. Morgan and Co., since he was fifteen, Peterkin had overheard many big deals being made by millionaires and had learned many "inside" secrets. He found that men with money needed only to be approached and then "sold" on any idea that sounded reasonable enough to succeed. Using his acquaintance with J. P. Morgan as a calling card, the young man quickly lined up an impressive list of men who were willing to invest in the Wright Company. Less than a month after Peterkin had first approached Wilbur, the company was officially formed. The agreement was that the Wrights would receive stock in the company plus a ten per cent royalty on the selling price of all planes sold. The main offices were to be in New York City but the planes would be produced in a factory at Dayton. Any infringements of their patents would be prosecuted by the Wright Company, and the company would bear all expenses of the resultant suits.

Legal suits against patent infringers had already been started by the Wrights. The first began in the fall of

1909, and before the suits ceased, the brothers were involved in about twenty different legal actions both at home and abroad. Most of these were quickly settled, but three of them—one each in France, England, and the United States—were especially noteworthy because they involved well-known personalities. The French case was brought against Louis Paulhan, a noted aviator, who planned to give demonstration flights in the United States using the basic Wright design, which was fully covered by patents in both countries. Another was against Claude Graham, British aviator, for the same reason. The most controversial action was that brought against the Herring-Curtiss Company and Glenn H. Curtiss himself. The Wrights won this case as they did all the others.

With the Wright Company now formed, and planes being produced at the Dayton factory at the rate of about two a month, the next task was to train pilots. Seeking a warmer climate for year-round training, Orville went to Montgomery, Alabama, in early 1910, and started a flying school west of the city. Today the field is known as Maxwell Air Force Base and is the home of the Air University, the Air Force's postgraduate education center.

Returning to Dayton in May, 1910, Orville, now thirty-nine, opened another flying school at Huffman Prairie. On May 21, Wilbur, at forty-three, made what turned out to be his last solo flight. On the twenty-fifth, the brothers broke their self-imposed rule against flying together and made their one and only flight with both men in the machine. In addition, on that same day Orville took their eighty-two-year-old father for his first and only flight—which made him the oldest man who had flown up to that time.

After all of their difficulties, the years 1909 and 1910 marked the beginning of true financial success. Between September, 1909, and the end of 1910, the Wrights had received over $200,000 in the United States alone. This included the $30,000 for the first Army plane, $15,000 for the flights up the Hudson, $100,000 for the organization of their company, and over $50,000 in dividends and royalties.

In spite of financial success, the Wrights were not content. Their time seemed to be completely taken up by business matters and there was no time for research and experimentation. They did not know it, but they would never again enjoy the freedom of brainstorming their ideas in the kitchen of their Dayton home. They had become famous and they had become rich. They had given birth to an exciting new era in world history, and the world would no longer permit them the luxury of being left alone.

The invention that they had brought to the world improved rapidly as other men experimented and pushed back the frontiers of aeronautical knowledge. In 1910 the speed of aircraft had increased to over a mile a minute; the nonstop flight record had suddenly jumped to an amazing 244 miles in 5 hours and 32 minutes; the altitude record had been set at 8,692 feet; and the power of engines had increased from 25–30 to almost 100 horsepower. By the end of the year the Alps had been crossed by air, flights had been made from London to Paris, and four passengers had been successfully carried aloft with the pilot.

It was ironic that the European nations were developing aircraft at a more rapid rate than the United States. All over the world, aviators were in the air trying to set new records and achieve new firsts. All over the world, that is, except the United States. But by 1911 the concern of the American public was getting to their congressmen. The continuing publicity of European flight achievements annoyed most Americans. When it was announced that the French government was going to appropriate $1,000,000 for aviation development, American congressmen voted the first appropriation specifically for military aviation. It totaled only $125,000, but it was a start.

By June, 1911, the nation's first military flying school was officially established at College Park, Maryland, and by the end of the year, the Army could boast of five planes and six pilots. These men had logged a total of 731 flights by the end of 1911, and 129 hours and 39 minutes of flying time. The top man was Lieutenant Foulois, for a time the nation's only military pilot. He had 52 hours in the air and had made 312 flights.

The entire year of 1911 was marked by more aviation records. Speed had increased to 80 miles an hour, distance to 400 miles, including cross-country flights from St. Louis to New York via Chicago. Endurance time aloft had increased to 14 hours, altitude to 13,000 feet, and the number of passengers to twelve. The hydroplane had been developed, and mail had been carried on exhibition runs both in the United States and Great Britain.

As these aeronautical records were being set, Orville and Wilbur Wright continued to protect their interests at home and in Europe. Orville mainly supervised plane production in Dayton, while Wilbur did the traveling. In March, 1911, Wilbur made a trip to Europe to prose-cute patent infringements. In October, after his return, Orville went once more to Kitty Hawk to experiment with an automatic control device on a glider. However, there were so many newsmen around that he never tested the device there for fear that it would be copied.

The gliding flights did produce a record that went virtually unnoticed in spite of the presence of newsmen looking for a story. On October 24, Orville stayed aloft for 9 minutes, 45 seconds, to set a soaring mark that stood for almost eleven years. The significance of this is not that a record went unnoticed but the fact that the Wrights were no longer front-page news. There were other men who designed and flew their own machines without directly infringing on the Wright patents. These men were more colorful, possessed much more ability to appeal to the crowds, and took far more risks than the Wrights ever would.

Of course, most of the new breed of daredevils were taking their risks in Wright machines. One of these was Galbraith P. "Cal" Rodgers, who had been trained at the Wright school in Dayton. Between September 7 and November 5, 1911, he made the first transconti-nental airplane trip from New York to California. Practically every landing was a crack-up but he made the 3,390 miles in only 84 hours' flying time—a re-markable feat considering the primitive state of aviation at the time.

The income that had suddenly piled up for the Wrights made them begin to plan for the future. They purchased land in a Dayton suburb and planned to build a new home where they hoped to retire from the strain of their business worries.

But shortly after the two brothers, their sister, and father visited the seventeen-acre site, Wilbur became ill. At first it was thought that he had only a slight fever caused by a cold. The fever hung on and was finally diagnosed by their family doctor as typhoid.

Wilbur's resistance was low. Worn out by traveling and never having been particularly healthy, he could not fight the fever. Specialists were called in, but in spite of the best medical knowledge then available, Wilbur Wright died in the early morning hours of May 30, 1912. He was only forty-five years old.

The death of half of the Wright team caused the world to pause a moment. Messages of condolence arrived at the Hawthorne Street house from all over the world. Kings, princes, paupers, and peasants expressed their sorrow to the bereaved family.

Bishop Wright, in his personal diary, tearfully noted the passing of his son, and described Wilbur as follows: "An unfailing intellect, imperturbable temper, great self-reliance and as great modesty, seeing the right clearly, pursuing it steadily, he lived and died." Later that year in reflecting on the past, the elder Wright wrote in his "Notes for 1912" that "In memory and intellect, there was none like him. He systematized everything. He could say or write anything he wanted to. He was not very talkative. His temper could hardly be stirred. He wrote much. He could deliver a fine speech, but was modest."

Perhaps Wilbur had sensed that death was near.

Only twenty days before he died he made out his last will and testament. He bequeathed fifty thousand dollars to each of his two older brothers and to his sister. To his father he left one thousand dollars "to use for little unusual expenditures as might add to his comfort and pleasure." Any residue after these bequests was left to Orville "who has been associated with me in all the hopes and labors of childhood and manhood, and who, I am sure, will use the property in very much the same manner as we would use it together in case we would both survive until old age. And for this reason, I make no specific bequest to charity."

Greatly saddened by the death of his brother, Orville gradually assumed the reins of the Wright Company as its president. With this burden now solely on his own shoulders, he faced the world of business with a long face and a heavy heart. Never again did Orville seriously experiment, devise, or invent. With the death of one brother, aviation had also lost the brilliance of the other.

CHAPTER IX

The Smithsonian Controversy

AFTER Wilbur's death, Orville, now forty-one, Katharine, and their father moved into the new house in Dayton, where Orville gamely tried to carry on the business without the benefit of his brother's counsel. He seldom flew, since more and more of his time was taken up with ground activities. As seemed to be the trend with so many early pilots who survived the primitive days of flying, Orville rarely got into a plane. His flights became so rare, in fact, that he attracted much attention from the press when he did fly. The last known flight that he made as a pilot took place in 1918 when he flew an early Wright biplane in formation with the newest plane of the day, the DH-4.

At the time of Wilbur's death, flying had become big business. Besides the lawsuits against infringers of the Wrights' plane design patents, would-be airplane manufacturers in Europe also copied the Wrights' control system and designs without benefit of license. Consequently, suits were brought against these infringers, including Bleriot, the first man to fly across the English Channel, and Santos-Dumont, the Brazilian.

The suits still dragged on in several foreign courts after Wilbur died, and caused Orville all kinds of mental anguish and personal unhappiness. Although he eventually won all of them, the necessity to continually protect himself and the Wright Company in the courts exhausted him. He withdrew more and more from public view.

In addition to the patent suits, Orville was exposed to the world of the "big business deal." The New York moneymen who had organized the Wright Company were, in Orville's eyes, schemers who wanted to use the company for political gain rather than for honest profit. This kind of political motivation was exemplified in one instance when the politicians running the company wanted to employ a lawyer to represent the firm in Washington. Upon inquiry, Orville learned that the selection was based, not on the man's ability, but on his supposed close acquaintance with President Woodrow Wilson.

It was this kind of political motivation that disgusted Orville, and he now wanted to retire from the company rather than be a part of it. However, he was a part of it because of the contract he had made. The only way out, he reasoned, was to buy out all of the other stockholders. He presented an unprecedented offer to those who had put up money for the incorporation of the firm. He would like to buy them out, he said, and was prepared to offer them enough, including the dividends they had already received, to give each man a profit of one hundred per cent. Were they interested?

They were. Consequently, Orville bought them all out with the exception of Robert J. Collier, a good friend. To pay for the reacquisition, Orville had to borrow money for the first time in his life. However, the deal was made and the company passed back into his hands.

In 1915, a few months after he had bought it back, Orville offered the company for sale. It was purchased by a syndicate headed by William Boyce Thompson and Frank Manville. Orville was retained as chief aeronautical engineer, with the understanding that he would be in charge of the company laboratory at Dayton.

The resale was personally satisfying to Orville because he realized the greatest profit of his life from this transaction. In addition, it allowed him to return to Dayton and experiment. After the papers were signed in October, 1915, Orville earnestly sought to submerge himself in his research activities. He built an office and workshop at 15 North Broadway, in downtown Dayton, which he used for the rest of his life.

One of the Wrights' basic successes had been their idea of building a wind tunnel to test their first control systems. The wind tunnel had been improved upon by others, so Orville decided to study the newest tunnels and testing methods that had come into use. In addition, since he had received the Aero Club of America Trophy for his invention of an automatic stabilizer in 1913, he experimented with his own system to see if it could be improved. In the midst of his pursuit of these and other projects, the United States declared war on Germany, and America joined the Allies in Europe to fight what became World War I.

When the Wrights had first flown successfully, neither of them realized nor predicted that their invention would someday revolutionize warfare. However, the warring European nations had found that their achievement of powered flight made possible the development of an aerial weapon that was capable of taking the offensive in modern war. At the outset of the war in 1914, however, the warring powers had little respect for aircraft as an offensive weapon. The British, French, and Germans alike at first thought of the air arm as "the cavalry of the sky"—a force that could reconnoiter the enemy quickly and report enemy troop movements to the ground commanders.

By the time the United States entered the war, airplanes had proven to be much more than the "eyes" of the ground forces. One air force took to the air to prevent the opposite side from carrying on its reconnaissance. At first, bricks were dropped by opposing aircraft. Then observers fired pistols and rifles at each other as the pilots maneuvered their planes into proper firing positions. By 1916, Germany had gained control of the air by taking advantage of an invention by the maker of the Fokker airplane. It was the development of a mechanism allowing machine-gun fire through a plane's propeller without hitting the blades. Thus, fixed guns fired by the pilot replaced the free fire of one plane upon another with rifles and pistols. The pilot could fly alone and fire against his adversary by aiming his whole plane and operating the guns himself.

The dropping of bricks from one airplane on another was quickly changed to the idea of an airplane dropping bombs on enemy ground forces. German planes bombed Compiègne in August, 1914, and three months later three English planes flew 250 miles over enemy territory to bomb the Zeppelin dirigible works at Friedrichshafen. The first cooperative effort between air and ground forces took place in September, 1915; night bombing from planes began a year later. Direction of artillery fire and aerial photography became increasingly important as the war progressed.

Orville watched each new use of the airplane with great interest. He was often asked what he thought of the warlike uses to which his flying machine had been put. In a letter dated June 21, 1917, he gave an interesting answer:

"When my brother and I built and flew the first man-carrying flying machine, we thought that we were introducing into the world an invention which would make further wars practically impossible. That we were not alone in this thought is evidenced by the fact that the French Peace Society presented us with medals on account of our invention. We thought governments would realize the impossibility of winning by surprise attacks, and that no country would enter into war with another of equal size when it knew that it would have to win by simply wearing out its enemy.

"Nevertheless, the world finds itself in the greatest war in history. Neither side has been able to win on account of the part the aeroplane has played. Both sides know exactly what the other is doing. The two sides are apparently nearly equal in aerial equipment, and it seems to me that unless present conditions can be changed, the war will continue for years.

"However, if the Allies' armies are equipped with such a number of aeroplanes as to keep the enemy planes entirely back of the line, so that they are unable to direct gunfire or to observe the movement of the Allied troops—in other words, if the enemy's eyes can be put out—it will be possible to end the war. This is not taking into account what might be done by bombing German sources of munition supplies, such as Essen, which is only about one hundred and fifty miles behind the fighting lines. But to end the war quickly and cheaply, the supremacy in the air must be so complete as to entirely blind the enemy." *

Such a letter from Orville Wright was a rarity. For all practical purposes, he had withdrawn from public view, and aeronautical progress was made without any further contributions from him. He appeared in public only on occasions commemorating the past. But his name crept into headlines many times between 1914 and 1948, the year of his death, because of a long and unhappy argument with the Smithsonian Institution in Washington. The controversy had started in 1901 and involved Samuel P. Langley.

Langley, a former professor of mathematics, physics, and astronomy, had become secretary of the Smithsonian in 1891 and had published the findings of his research in aerodynamics. He hoped, through his calculations and actual flight experiments, to prove that

* Letter, Orville Wright to C. H. Hitchcock, Washington, D.C.

heavier-than-air flight was possible. He came to the conclusion that Newton's law—the resistance of a plane surface to the air varies as the square of the sine of its angle of incidence—was incorrect. He also concluded that air resistance was only one-twentieth of that indicated by Newton, and that less power would be required to sustain a machine in flight at high speed than at low speed. History has proven Langley wrong, but the fact that he was a true man of science gave him the backing of the Smithsonian, which meant money as well as the resources to pursue his experiments. His writings on the subject attracted much attention, including that of the Wright brothers. Wilbur Wright acknowledged this in a 1906 letter to Octave Chanute, in which he recalled that "the knowledge that the head of the most prominent scientific institution of America believed in the possibility of human flight was one of the influences that led us to undertake the preliminary investigation that preceded our active work."

Langley called his machine an "aerodrome." He used a steam engine and, between 1893 and 1903, progressed from flying models to a man-carrying machine. He failed miserably and often but he persisted. Crashes were so frequent as to be almost expected. Changing to a gasoline engine opened up new avenues of power possibilities, so that by the summer of 1903 the Langley machine, with Charles Manly, a Cornell University engineering graduate as pilot, was ready for what was widely heralded as the first successful powered man-flight in history.

The Langley aerodrome was loaded aboard a houseboat to be towed down the Potomac River from Washington to a point opposite Widewater, Virginia. Spurning launching rails or a catapult, Langley had reasoned that he needed a platform, such as the top of the houseboat provided, to overcome the original inertia of being at rest.

The first trial did not take place until October 7. Seating himself in the "aviator's car," Manly started the engine and waited until it warmed up. At his signal, a helper cut the cable holding the craft to the deck and Manly leaped forward. A second later the fragile craft was a mass of wreckage as it hit the water and folded around the pilot. Manly was rescued but the machine was a mess.

By December 8 the wreckage had been rebuilt and the game Manly was ready to try again. An official observer for the Army gave this eyewitness report to his superiors:

"The car was set in motion and the propellers revolved rapidly, the engine working perfectly, but there was something wrong with the launching, and a crashing, rending sound, followed by the collapse of the rear wings, showed that the machine had been wrecked in the launching, just how it was impossible for me to see. The fact remains that the rear wings and rudder were wrecked before the machine was free of the ways."

Again Manly had to be fished from the Potomac. He was never to make another attempt. The Army, up to that time convinced that Langley's ideas had merit, had invested fifty thousand dollars. When the observer's report was received, the War Department was quick to announce that it was "not prepared to make an additional allotment at this time for continuing this work."

The press was quick to ridicule Langley's failure. One writer, using an inaccurate money figure, said: "Here is $100,000 of the people's money wasted on this scientific aerial navigation experiment because some man, perchance a professor wandering in his dreams, was able to impress officers that his scheme had some utility.

"Perhaps if the professor had only thought to launch his airship bottom up, it would have gone into the air instead of down into the water."

It was into this atmosphere of disbelief and ridicule that the Wright brothers had dared to venture. Nine days after the failure of the Langley machine, the Wrights succeeded. Paradoxically, they had achieved what Langley knew was possible, but they had done it without the advantages of Langley's engineering knowledge, the resources of the Smithsonian Institution, or government financing.

Dr. Langley died in 1906. To commemorate his connection with the Smithsonian, and his unflagging perseverance, the Board of Regents authorized the installation of a tablet in his memory, to be placed in a prominent location in the Smithsonian Institution. Dr. Charles D. Walcott, who followed Langley as secretary, wrote to the Wrights asking their opinion on a proposed inscription giving credit to "Langley's Law." Knowing that Langley's computations were incorrect, Wilbur answered that it would be unfair to Langley to give him credit for erroneous computations. He suggested that reference to "Langley's Law" be deleted.

Dr. Walcott agreed to the deletion and substituted a phrase that credited Langley with having "discovered the relations of speed and angle of inclination to the lifting power of surfaces moving in the air." This discovery was not Dr. Langley's. The Wrights were now certain that the Smithsonian was determined to give Langley credit where it was not deserved, and that Dr. Walcott was firmly convinced that the Wrights did not deserve credit for having discovered the secret of flight and having performed the original research that made the flying machine possible. The result was a bitter and unnecessary controversy.

CHAPTER X

The Fate of the Flyer

✌ ✌ ✌ ✌

HISTORIANS have tried to rationalize the reasons for the controversy between the Smithsonian Institution and the Wrights. The fact remains, however, that after the death of Dr. Langley, the Smithsonian carried on a campaign to discredit the claims of the Wright brothers that they had built the first truly successful flying machine.

To add fuel to the growing disenchantment, the Smithsonian turned down the Wrights' offer of the original Wright Flyer. As its chief spokesman, Dr. Walcott seemed unable to admit that the Wright machine, and not Dr. Langley's, was the first man-carrying, heavier-than-air craft. After Wilbur's death, the matter was dropped until 1916.

The controversy flared anew when the 1903 Flyer was displayed at the Massachusetts Institute of Technology. One of the viewers was Alexander Graham Bell, who was surprised to learn that the first Wright plane was still intact. As a member of the Board of Regents for the Smithsonian, Bell asked why Orville did not offer it to the Smithsonian Institution for permanent display.

"But, Dr. Bell," Orville replied, "the Smithsonian does not want it."

"I think you are wrong," Bell told him. "You shall soon hear from Dr. Walcott."

Walcott did write, and a meeting was arranged. However, Orville sensed the animosity and reluctance of the secretary to have the original Wright machine exhibited alongside the Langley aerodrome. Walcott felt that he had good reason to refuse at this time because, two years previously, Glenn Curtiss had lost a patent suit to the Wrights and had tried to prove that Langley's machine really could fly. Curtiss was permitted to take the aerodrome to Hammondsport, New York, where the plane was modified and rebuilt. In May and June, 1914, he was able to get it airborne for a few seconds.

Using the word of witnesses that the Langley machine had flown, and ignoring the changes that were made to the original in order to make it flyable, Walcott issued a report that year announcing that the aerodrome had flown "without modification." Also reported was the information that "It [the Langley aerodrome] has demonstrated that with its original structure and power, it is capable of flying with a pilot and several hundred pounds of useful load. It is the first aeroplane in the history of the world of which this can truthfully be said."

The next year the annual Smithsonian report contained another surprising statement. It said that "the tests thus far have shown that former Secretary Langley had succeeded in building the first aeroplane capable of sustained free flight with a man." The Langley machine was brought back to the Smithsonian, returned to its original condition, and again put on display. The result was that many historians and writers began to give Langley credit for the discovery that belonged to the Wrights.

The original Flyer was stored in Dayton. It remained there through the years while Orville patiently waited for someone to correct the facts and give him and his brother the credit they had earned, and which had been well established in the many patent cases they had won. By 1923, however, nothing had been done and a request was received from the Science Museum in London to display the Wright machine. Reluctantly, Orville decided that he would grant the request.

The result of his announcement was a flood of letters from all over the country saying, in effect, that it was un-American to let the British have what rightfully belonged to the United States. Orville's reaction was as follows:

"In a foreign museum this machine will be a constant reminder of the reason for its being there, and after the people and petty jealousies of this day are gone, the historians of the future may examine impartially the evidence and make history accord with it.

"Your regret that this old machine must leave our country can hardly be so great as my own."

Although Orville had agreed to send the Flyer to London, he delayed doing so for five years. Then, in 1928, fourteen years after the tests by Curtiss, when it seemed certain that the Smithsonian would not correct its records, the fragile plane was shipped across the Atlantic. Still hopeful that public demand would cause it to be returned, Orville agreed that the Science Museum could keep it for at least five years, and perhaps longer, unless he personally requested that it be returned during his lifetime.

Although Dr. Walcott died in 1927, and his successor, Dr. Charles G. Abbot, wanted to right the wrong that had been perpetrated, nothing was done. The years dragged by and still no action was taken either to correct the Smithsonian's records or request that the Wright machine be returned. World War II started in Europe and the Flyer was put in protective storage to prevent it from being destroyed by German air raids.

In September, 1942, Dr. Abbot prepared a statement to the Board of Regents which was acceptable to Orville. The statement fully acknowledged the unfair 1914 experiments at Hammondsport, saying that: "It is to be regretted that the Institution published statements repeatedly to the effect that these experiments of 1914 demonstrated that Langley's plane of 1903 without essential modification was the first heavier-than-air machine capable of maintaining sustained human flight."

Dr. Abbot made a detailed comparison between the 1903 and 1914 Langley machines and fully apologized for the former untrue statements and distortions. His final paragraph marked the end of the long controversy: "If the publication of this paper should clear the way for Dr. Wright to bring back to America the Kitty Hawk machine to which all the world awards first place, it will be a source of profound and enduring gratification to his countrymen everywhere. Should he decide to deposit the plane in the United States National Museum, it would be given the highest place of honor, which is its due."

The risks of loss were too great to have the Flyer brought back during World War II. However, plans were made, and Orville hoped that he would see their machine on display before he died. He never realized this desire. On January 30, 1948, at 10:30 P.M., he suffered a heart attack and died. The next December 17, on the forty-fifth anniversary of the historic flight, the famous Flyer was unveiled in the main building of the Smithsonian and the unhappy argument officially ended.

The inscription on the exhibition plaque does not give any clues to the story behind it, but the words leave no doubt that the Smithsonian Institution fully recognizes what the Wrights did for the world:

THE ORIGINAL WRIGHT BROTHERS' AEROPLANE

THE WORLD'S FIRST

POWER-DRIVEN HEAVIER-THAN-AIR MACHINE IN WHICH MAN

MADE FREE, CONTROLLED, AND SUSTAINED FLIGHT

INVENTED AND BUILT BY WILBUR AND ORVILLE WRIGHT

FLOWN BY THEM AT KITTY HAWK, NORTH CAROLINA

DECEMBER 17, 1903

BY ORIGINAL, SCIENTIFIC RESEARCH, THE WRIGHT BROTHERS

DISCOVERED THE PRINCIPLES OF HUMAN FLIGHT

AS INVENTORS, BUILDERS, AND FLYERS,

THEY FURTHER DEVELOPED THE AEROPLANE, TAUGHT MAN TO

FLY, AND OPENED THE ERA OF AVIATION.

In the history of civilization, relatively few years have passed since that cold December morning at Kitty Hawk. In that time, the Wright Flyer has evolved into the world's greatest force for understanding and peace among men. It has also become the force with which man may blast himself into extinction. The follow-on scientific achievements which have occurred since the Wright breakthrough have been phenomenal. Ironically, all of them—the harnessing of the atom, jet propulsion, missiles, helicopters, and space flight—can paint a dream for the future in which the peoples of the world will find harmony together. On the other hand, the same brush can paint a nightmare of hatred, despair, and death. The airplane, conceived by the Wrights as a machine of peace, has become a decisive force for peace or war. Only man can decide which.

Chronology

1867   April 16, Wilbur Wright born

1871   August 19, Orville Wright born

1892   Wright brothers open bicycle shop

1896   Begin glider experiments

1899   Construct glider with "warped wings"

1900   Construct man-carrying glider; begin experiments at Kitty Hawk, North Carolina; meet Octave Chanute, pioneer in aeronautics

1901   Experiment at Kitty Hawk with new, larger glider; realize air pressure tables are wrong; devise new tables; construct wind tunnel

1902   Experiment at Kitty Hawk with still larger glider; set number of world records in controllable glider

1903   December 17, both brothers successfully fly in powered machine; apply for U. S. patent

1904   Test flights with new plane near Dayton, Ohio; first use catapult; apply for foreign patents

1906   U. S. patent granted

1907   War Department establishes Aeronautical Division

1908   Brothers win Army bid to demonstrate flying machine and train pilots; May 14, take up first passenger; Wilbur goes to France to demonstrate plane, breaks many records; Orville demonstrates plane for Army; crash kills passenger

1909   Orville and sister join Wilbur in Europe; return home to finish Army tests; complete tests in Germany; Wright Company formed

1910   Orville begins flying schools near Montgomery, Alabama; and Dayton, Ohio.
1911   U. S. government votes for military aviation for the first time; establishes first military flying school, College Park, Maryland
1912   May 30, Wilbur dies at the age of forty-five
1915   Orville buys Wright Company outright
1916   Airplane makes mark in World War I; controversy begins between Wright and Smithsonian Institution
1918   Orville makes last flight as pilot
1923   Orville agrees to send original plane to London museum
1928   Original Flyer shipped to London
1948   January 30, Orville dies; December 17, Flyer returned to U. S. and Smithsonian Institution

For Further Reading

Freudenthal, Elspeth E. *Flight into History: The Wright Brothers and the Air Age.* Norman, Oklahoma: University of Oklahoma Press, 1949.

Harrison, Michael. *Airborne at Kittyhawk.* London: Cassell, 1953.

Kelly, Fred C. *Miracle at Kitty Hawk: The Letters of Wilbur and Orville Wright.* New York: Farrar, Straus, 1951.

Tillman, Stephen F. *Man Unafraid.* Washington, D.C.: Army Times Publishing Co., 1958.

Wright, Orville. *How We Invented the Airplane.* New York: David McKay, 1953.

INDEX